Exploring Science 1

Mark Levesley
Sandra Baggley
Julian Clarke
Steve Gray
Marc Pimbert

Longman

Edinburgh Gate
Harlow, Essex

Contents

Physics

How to use this book

You should be able to answer this question by the time you have finished the work on the page.

C1b Things are hotting up

How can we make things dissolve faster?

Some people add sugar to their tea and coffee to make it taste sweet. They are not interested in the total amount of sugar that could possibly dissolve in the water. The most important thing is to get the sugar to dissolve quickly.

 1 If you want the sugar in your tea to dissolve quickly, what do you do?

Three important factors (or **variables**) affect the time it takes for something to dissolve:
- the temperature of the water
- the size of the pieces
- whether you stir the water or not.

Some questions are spread around the page so you can answer them as you read through the topic.

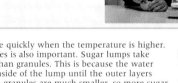 **P.** How would you find out how each of these factors changes the time that sugar takes to dissolve?
- How would you make it a fair test?

Practical boxes give you ideas for investigations or other practical work. Sometimes there is a picture to give you some ideas for planning your investigation.

Solids dissolve more quickly when the temperature is higher. The size of the pieces is also important. Sugar lumps take longer to dissolve than granules. This is because the water cannot get to the inside of the lump until the outer layers have dissolved. The granules are much smaller, so more sugar is in contact with the water.

 2 An experiment is carried out to investigate whether granules dissolve faster than lumps. Write down three factors that would need to be kept the same to make it a fair test.

Even granules won easily if they are at bottom of the cup, by another layer of the water cannot ge them. So, stirring w help the sugar to di Stirring moves the around so that they with the water.

 3 In which of thes sugar dissolve fa in each case:
a) 1 lump of su of sugar in w
b) 5 g of sugar i granules, eac

If you open a warm often 'froth up'. Thi soluble in warm wa drink warms up, the the solution. If the l cannot escape – unt

 4 The instructions 'Open with care and cover the to sunlight. Best se Explain why it sa

 Oxygen from the ai gills to take this oxy Many fish die in ver there is less oxygen

The questions at the end of the page may be a little harder, so you can see if you have understood the work.

If you need to find information about something, use the **index** on pages 160–161. If you need to find out what a word means, use the **glossary** on pages 154–159.

B1c Focus on: Temperature control

How do animals control their body temperatures?

Some animals are **cold-blooded** and others are **warm-blooded**.

Warm-blooded animals can

Marine iguanas are cold-blooded

Arctic foxes are warm-blooded

1 What helps to stop heat escaping from:
   a) mammals   b) birds?

2 Why must warm-blooded animals eat more when it is cold?

...ooded animals may need to ...eat by sweating. Dogs cannot

...tiles are **cold-blooded**. ...depend on the temperature of ...les often sun-bathe to warm up.

...move very fast when it is cold, ... iguana gets too hot it will sit ...wim!

Humans have a constant body temperature of 37 °C. Temperatures above 38 °C mean that we are ill. Temperatures below 35 °C cause a serious condition called **hypothermia**.

Claude Bernard (1813–1878) worked out how mammals control their body temperatures.

...brates is the iguana?
...of five cold-blooded ...vertebrates.

...aining how the human ...ture the same.

...ple do:
...it is cold
...t is hot.

...odiles rest with their

11

c) 10 g of sugar granules in 100 cm³ of water with stirring, or without stirring.

d) 10 g of sugar in 100 cm³ of water, or 10 g of sugar in 250 cm³ of water.

You should know...
● You can make something dissolve more quickly by stirring it, by crushing it into smaller pieces, or by heating the water.

61

What do all living things do?

Scientists think that the first living things appeared on Earth about 3000 million years ago. Many scientists now believe that life may have developed on other planets as well.

There could be about 10 thousand million million planets in the Universe! A lot of money is being spent to explore space to try to find life on other planets.

NASA is sending many spacecraft to Mars to find out if there was ever life on the planet. This is a drawing of the Mars Polar Lander.

 1 When did living things first appear on Earth?

Some people think that the Earth has been visited by aliens from another planet. They think that the aliens travel in Unidentified Flying Objects (UFOs).

 2 What might an alien look for in a human, to find out if it was a living thing?

 Crypto-zoology is the scientific search for unknown animals.

In 1993, this large animal called the Vu Quang was discovered in the forests of Vietnam.

Dr Bill Gibbons, a crypto-zoologist, believes that dinosaurs still exist in parts of central Africa. He regularly goes dinosaur hunting in the swamps along the River Congo.

There are still plenty of undiscovered living things on Earth. Thousands of different plants and animals live in tropical rainforests. Scientists find over 100 new sorts of living things each week in these areas.

If scientists think they have found a new type of living thing, they must make sure that it really is living! Living things are called **organisms**. There are seven things that something must be able to do before it can be called an organism. These are called 'life processes'.

 How would you prove that plants can move towards light?
- How will you grow your seeds?
- How will you get light to come from one direction only?

Movement. Organisms **move**. Plants can move some of their parts. Sunflowers turn to follow the Sun during the day

Reproduction. Organisms **reproduce** (they make more living things like themselves)

Sensitivity. Organisms **sense** and react to things around them

Growth. Organisms **grow**

Respiration. Organisms **respire**. They need oxygen and food to make energy for themselves.

Excretion. Organisms **excrete** waste. They produce substances that they do not need and so they must get rid of them

Nutrition. Organisms require **nutrition**. They need various substances to help them respire and grow

3 Copy the table below and write the following things in the correct column:

car, cow, chair, mouse, sunflower, goldfish, robot, gerbil, Sun, rock, octopus, coal.

Living	Non-living

4 What do we mean by the word '**organism**'?

5 Which life process does each of the following describe:
a) a dog running in the park
b) a plant making seeds
c) a mouse finding cheese by smelling
d) an acorn becoming an oak tree
e) a cow eating grass.

6 Write down three life processes that a cow does but a car does not.

7 This is the Martian Rover, a robot that NASA sent to Mars to discover more about the planet. It can sense rocks so that it can move around them as it travels along the ground taking pictures and other scientific measurements. It uses a battery as a source of power.

a) What features about the Rover might suggest to a Martian that it is a living thing?
b) How would a Martian know that the Rover was not a living thing?

You should know…

● **Living things are called organisms.**

● **Organisms must do all of these things: Move, Reproduce, use their Senses, Grow, Respire, Excrete waste, take in Nutrition.**

● **You can remember all seven of these using the phrase 'Mrs Gren'.**

How do scientists divide living things into groups?

It is hard to imagine life in a world where things are not grouped together. Things are grouped in our homes, in shops, in libraries and on computer hard disks. Grouping things (called **classification**) makes them easier to find again.

Scientists **classify** living things. The first set of groups that organisms are divided into are called **kingdoms**. The two largest kingdoms are the **plant kingdom** and the **animal kingdom**.

*Some members of the **animal kingdom***

*Some members of the **plant kingdom***

1 What do scientists call grouping things together?

2 What are kingdoms?

3 Which are the two largest kingdoms?

There are many different ways of telling plants and animals apart. The main difference that scientists use is that plants can make their own food, using energy from the Sun. Animals cannot do this.

4 Write down two ways in which plants and animals are:
 a) similar b) different.

There are so many different types of animals on Earth that the **animal kingdom** is divided into smaller groups. One of these groups contains all the animals that have backbones. Animals with backbones are called **vertebrates**. If you run your hand down the middle of your back, the bumps you feel are the parts of your backbone. Therefore humans are part of the vertebrate group.

There are a large number of **vertebrate**s and so the group is divided into smaller groups called **amphibians**, **birds**, **fish**, **mammals** and **reptiles**.

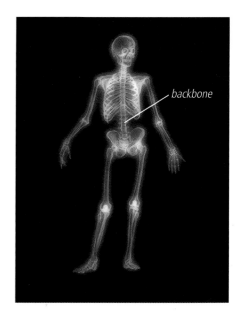
backbone

The modern way of classifying plants and animals was invented in 1735 by Carl Linnaeus.

You can use a **branching** or **spider key** to work out which group something belongs to.

Branching keys take up a lot of room and so it is often better to use a **statement key**. Use the statement key to work out which group the snake belongs to.

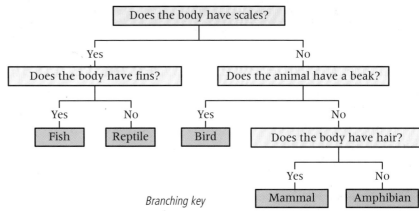

Branching key

You should know…

- **Dividing things into groups is called classification.**

- **Living things are divided into kingdoms. Members of the plant kingdom can make their own food, animals cannot.**

- **Vertebrates are animals that have backbones.**

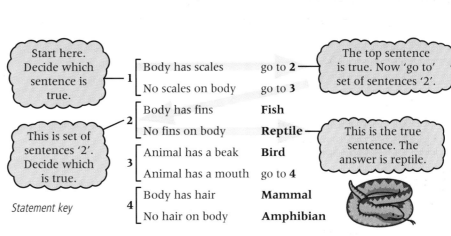

Statement key

---

5 a) Copy the table below. Decide which group each of the animals belongs to and write its name in the correct column. Use the keys on this page to help you.

Amphibians	Birds	Fish	Mammals	Reptiles

Parrot

Dolphin

Tortoise

Toad   Angel fish   Human   Monitor lizard   Seagull

b) Write down which two animals you found the most difficult to group and explain why.

6 Use the statement key below to identify these fish.

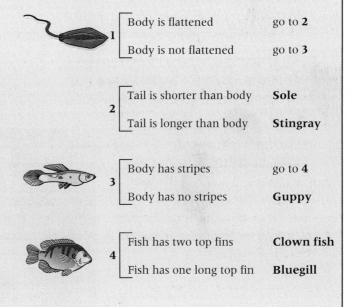

1	Body is flattened	go to **2**
	Body is not flattened	go to **3**
2	Tail is shorter than body	**Sole**
	Tail is longer than body	**Stingray**
3	Body has stripes	go to **4**
	Body has no stripes	**Guppy**
4	Fish has two top fins	**Clown fish**
	Fish has one long top fin	**Bluegill**

What are the differences between the vertebrate groups?

Most keys use differences that you can easily see. But there are many other differences between the vertebrate groups that you cannot see.

THE VERTEBRATES

AMPHIBIANS
• Have moist skin
• Lay eggs in water
• Eggs coated in jelly
• Cold blooded

BIRDS
• Have feathers
• Eggs have a hard shell
• Warm blooded

FISH
• Have wet scales
• Live in water
• Have fins to move
• Breathe using gills
• Cold blooded

MAMMALS
• Have hair
• Give birth to live young
• Produce milk
• Warm blooded

REPTILES
• Have dry scales
• Eggs have a leathery shell
• Cold blooded

Each different type of animal (or plant) is called a **species**.
Lions and tigers are both mammals but they are different species.

1 Which features are the same in birds and reptiles, and which are different?

2 a) What are animals with backbones called?
   b) What groups are they divided into?
   c) Write down two examples from each group.

3 Which group or groups of vertebrates:
   a) do not lay eggs   b) lay eggs in water
   c) have scales   d) are warm blooded?

4 Dolphins and dogs are both mammals but look very different:
   a) Write down the differences between humans, dolphins and dogs.
   b) Write down their similarities.
   c) Say why you think a dolphin is a mammal.

Dinosaurs were reptiles. They died out 65 million years ago and nobody knows why! Some people think that there are still dinosaurs left.

The Loch Ness Monster is claimed to be a dinosaur. This picture, however, is a fake!

Jean-Baptiste Lamarck (1744–1829) was the first person to put animals with backbones into their own group (the vertebrates) in 1822. He also invented the word 'biology'!

You should know...
● **The main features of amphibians, birds, fish, mammals and reptiles.**
● **Each different type of animal (or plant) is called a species.**

How do animals control their body temperatures?

Some animals are **cold-blooded** and others are **warm-blooded**.

Warm-blooded animals can keep themselves warm in the cold. Birds and mammals are warm-blooded. Some of the food that they eat is used to make heat. Feathers and hair help to stop the heat escaping.

On cold days humans shiver. Shivering causes our muscles to move, making more heat.

Marine iguanas are cold-blooded

Arctic foxes are warm-blooded

1 What helps to stop heat escaping from:
   a) mammals   b) birds?

2 Why must warm-blooded animals eat more when it is cold?

If it is very hot, warm-blooded animals may need to lose heat. Humans lose heat by sweating. Dogs cannot sweat – they pant instead.

Amphibians, fish and reptiles are **cold-blooded**. Their body temperatures depend on the temperature of their surroundings. Reptiles often sun-bathe to warm up.

A marine iguana cannot move very fast when it is cold, so it lies in the sun. If the iguana gets too hot it will sit in the shade or go for a swim!

Humans have a constant body temperature of 37 °C. Temperatures above 38 °C mean that we are ill. Temperatures below 35 °C cause a serious condition called **hypothermia**.

Claude Bernard (1813–1878) worked out how mammals control their body temperatures.

3 In which group of vertebrates is the iguana?

4 Write down the names of five cold-blooded and five warm-blooded vertebrates.

5 Write a paragraph explaining how the human body keeps its temperature the same.

6 Write a list of things people do:
   a) to keep warm when it is cold
   b) to cool down when it is hot.

7 Try to find out why crocodiles rest with their mouths open.

Mammals as pets

How should we care for our pet mammals?

Cats and dogs are the most popular pets in the United Kingdom. People enjoy the company of their pets but looking after them can take up a lot of time and be expensive.

Dogs have lived with humans for over 12 000 years. In Ancient Egypt they were sacred animals. Today, dogs are used for guarding, for searching, for helping blind people and for friendship.

Dogs need good food and fresh water every day. They need plenty of exercise to stop their muscles becoming weak. They also need to be kept clean. Regular washing and brushing helps to get rid of small blood-sucking insects, like fleas. These live in the hair and make the skin sore. Regular trips to the vet will find problems before they get too serious.

Dogs can smell things about 40 times better than we can and so they are used by the police to search for things like drugs.

Fleas are blood-sucking insects that can live on cats and dogs. This one is photographed sitting on the end of a doctor's needle (magnification ×40).

Cats need less looking after than dogs. They wash themselves and don't need to be taken for walks! However, they still need food and water, and regular trips to the vet.

1 What are dogs used for?

2 How can you make sure a pet dog stays healthy?

3 Find out some more information about a pet. Some things you might find out are: what it eats, when it feeds, whether it needs anything special, when it last went to the vet, what illnesses it has had.

Many dogs and cats get worms, like tapeworms, hookworms and roundworms. These live in the intestines of animals and can make them very sick. Worms can be treated with tablets from a vet.

A canine (dog) roundworm

What are invertebrates?

Apart from the vertebrates, there are another eight major groups of animals! Animals in these other groups do not have backbones. They are **invertebrates**.

A crab is an invertebrate. It has no backbone. Its skeleton is on the outside, as this x-ray shows.

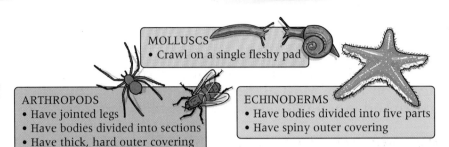

MOLLUSCS
• Crawl on a single fleshy pad

ARTHROPODS
• Have jointed legs
• Have bodies divided into sections
• Have thick, hard outer covering

ECHINODERMS
• Have bodies divided into five parts
• Have spiny outer covering

THERE ARE EIGHT GROUPS OF INVERTEBRATES

CNIDARIANS
• Have thin sack like bodies
• Have tentacles

ANNELIDS
• Have round, worm-like bodies
• Have bodies divided into segments

FLATWORMS
• Have flat, worm-like bodies

ROUNDWORMS
• Have long, thin, round worm-like bodies
• Have bodies with no segments

SPONGES
• Have bodies made of loosely joined cells

1 Copy the table and write the names of these invertebrates in the correct column.

Arthropods	Echinoderms	Molluscs

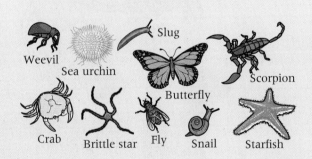

Weevil, Sea urchin, Slug, Butterfly, Scorpion, Crab, Brittle star, Fly, Snail, Starfish

2 Look at these animals. For each one write down which group you think it belongs to and why.

Lobster   Leech

3 For each of these lists of organisms, write down which is the odd one out and why.
a) snail   reindeer   pig   oak tree   sponge
b) tapeworm   slug   wasp   eagle   starfish
c) sea urchin   fly   spider   ant   lobster
d) dolphin   salmon   seagull   lobster   crocodile
e) bear   horse   pig   hamster   frog

The longest animal ever discovered was a ribbon worm, found on a Scottish beach in 1864. It was 55 m long!

You should know...
● Invertebrates are animals without backbones.
● The main features of arthropods, echinoderms and molluscs.

What groups can arthropods be divided into?

Scientists have identified about 800 000 different animal species on Earth. Most of these are **arthropods**. The **arthropod** group is divided into four smaller groups.

A crab is a **crustacean** (pronounced 'crust-**ay**-shun'). Crustaceans have between five and seven pairs of legs. The first pair of legs are often used as pincers! Their bodies are covered in a chalky shell

A spider is an **arachnid** (pronounced 'ar-**ack**-nid'). Arachnids have four pairs of legs, no wings and bodies that are divided into two sections

A wasp is an **insect**. Insects have three pairs of legs and bodies that are divided into three sections. They often have wings

Centipedes and millipedes have long, thin bodies with pairs of legs on each of their many body sections

!
Many animals have shells for protection. However, shells are no protection against the Mantis shrimp. This grows up to 20 cm long and one blow from its hammer-like claw is so powerful it has been known to break human finger bones and thick aquarium glass.

Although the groups are very different, all arthropods have jointed legs and a hard outer covering (called an **exoskeleton**).

1 Look at the picture of the Mantis shrimp in the picture above. Which group do you think it belongs to and why?

2 Here is a list of organisms:
butterfly, cow, crab, daffodil, eagle, snail, spider, starfish
Using the words below, write down all the groups that each one belongs to.

amphibian	animal	annelid	arachnid	arthropod	bird
centipede	crustacean	echinoderm	fish	flatworm	insect
invertebrate	jellyfish	mammal	mollusc	plant	reptile
roundworm	sponge	vertebrate			

You should know...

● The arthropods are split into four smaller groups: arachnids, crustaceans, insects, and centipedes and millipedes.

● The main features of these groups.

What are the main features of insects?

Insect bodies have three parts:
head, **thorax** and **abdomen**.

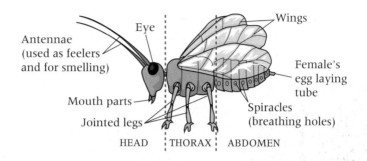

Antennae
(used as feelers
and for smelling)

Eye

Wings

Female's
egg laying
tube

Mouth parts

Jointed legs

Spiracles
(breathing holes)

HEAD   THORAX   ABDOMEN

Attached to the **thorax** are six legs and usually one or two pairs of wings. The **abdomen** has a series of small holes (**spiracles**) along it. These let air in. The reproductive organs and anus (for getting rid of waste) are at the end of the abdomen.

The hard exoskeleton cannot stretch and so insects have to grow in stages. Some insects, like grasshoppers, have young (**larvae**) which look like the adults. To grow, they have to shed their exoskeletons and build bigger ones. This is called **moulting**.

The larvae of many other insects do not look like the adults. They are simple, tube-shaped creatures which can moult easily. These larvae turn into **pupae**. An adult is formed inside a pupa. The series of changes, from larva to adult, is called **metamorphosis**.

 1 What are the three parts of an insect's body?

2 Why do insects need to let air into their bodies?

 Crickets 'chirp' by rubbing their wings together. They chirp faster on warmer days. You can work out the temperature (in °C) by counting the chirps! Take the number of chirps per minute, divide by 4, add 8, and then divide by 1.8!

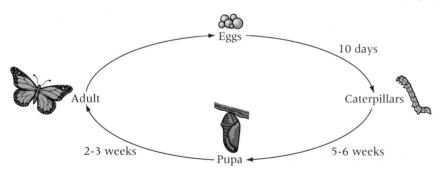

Eggs

10 days

Adult

Caterpillars

2-3 weeks

Pupa

5-6 weeks

 3 Write down the seven 'life processes'. Which parts of an insect help with each one?

4 a) What would the temperature be if a cricket made the following number of chirps in each minute:
i) 112   ii) 134   iii) 184?

b) How many chirps per minute would you expect at:
i) 15 °C   ii) 25 °C   iii) 35 °C?
(Multiply by 1.8, subtract 8 then multiply by 4.)

c) Draw a graph showing how the number of chirps increases with temperature.

What groups are plants divided into?

Three of the life processes for all living things are **movement**, **reproduction** and **growth**.

 1 Write down an example of plant movement.

*Parts of plants can **move**. These flowers close up at night*

Plants make new plants. They **reproduce**. There are four groups of plants.

Ferns also reproduce using spores.

spore containers

Fern

Mosses reproduce using **spores**. Each spore can grow into a new moss plant. Spores are so small that you can hardly see them.

spores

Moss

Conifers use **seeds** to reproduce. The seeds are found in **cones**. Each seed can grow into a new conifer plant. Seeds are much bigger than spores and you can easily see them.

needles

seed

Conifer

Flowering plants also make seeds. The seeds are found in **fruits**.

flat leaves

seed

Flowering plant

 2 Look at the four pictures above:
   a) Write down one way in which mosses and ferns are similar.
   b) Write down two differences between conifers and flowering plants.

3 Make a list of all seven life processes.

P How would you show that seeds respire?
- What gas will you test for?
- What liquid do you need to test for this gas?

A plant is built from millions of **cells** (which you can only see using a **microscope**). Every cell has to have energy. They use **respiration** to get energy. Respiration uses up food and oxygen. Carbon dioxide is made at the same time.

During the day, plants make their own food (**sugar**) in their leaves using energy from the Sun. This is called **photosynthesis**. Photosynthesis needs **water** and **carbon dioxide**.

Carbon dioxide from the air enters the leaves through tiny holes, called **stomata**. The stomata also let waste gases out (**excretion**).

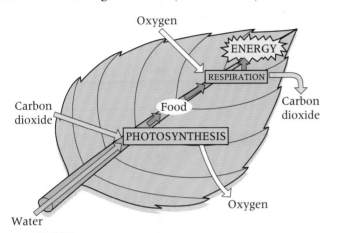

Trees can be conifers or flowering plants. *The tallest flowering plants in the world are Eucalyptus trees in Tasmania. They can grow up to 150 m tall.*

The water is absorbed from the soil by the roots. In most plants it is carried to the leaves in special tubes called **xylem tubes** (pronounced 'z-**eye**-lem').

4 a) Which life process happens in every cell?
b) What process do plants use to make food (for their **nutrition**)?

Mosses do not have roots or xylem tubes. They have thin leaves which lose a lot of water.

Ferns have roots and xylem tubes. They have many small, waterproof leaves that don't lose much water.

Flowering plants have roots and xylem tubes. They have large flat, waterproof leaves. Most plants are flowering plants, but some of the flowers are difficult to spot.
For example, grass is a flowering plant – grass flowers are green and not brightly coloured.

Conifers have roots and xylem tubes. They have waterproof, needle-shaped leaves.

5 a) What do xylem tubes do?
b) Which plant groups have xylem tubes?

6 Why do mosses grow best in damp places?

7 Write down the names of the four plant groups. For each group, make a list of its features. You can draw pictures if you wish.

You should know...

● The main features of mosses, ferns, conifers and flowering plants, and how they reproduce.

● Plants make their own food using energy from the sun in a process called photosynthesis.

What can we use plants for?

Plants have thousands of uses. For example, flowers are used to decorate our homes. Many plants are eaten as food.

 Although some plants can be eaten, many are deadly poisonous. Never eat parts of any plant that you find in the countryside.

Wheat seeds are ground to make flour. Bread is made from flour

 1 a) Write down the names of 10 plants that you can eat.
   b) Add to your list which part of each plant you eat.

Parts of some plants have strong flavours and are used in small amounts to give extra flavour to food. These are known as **herbs** and **spices**.

Mint leaves, cinnamon bark and the fruit of the vanilla plant are all used as flavourings for food

Many flowers have a pleasant scent. This scent can be used to make perfumes. Rosewater and lavender oil are scents made from the petals of plants.

Many plants are used to make drinks. Fruits are often squeezed to make fruit juices. Other parts of plants can be turned into alcoholic drinks. For example, the fruits of the hop plant are used to make beer and potatoes can be used to make vodka.

Many fabrics and textiles are made out of plants. The fruits from cotton plants are used to make cotton. Much of our clothing is made of cotton.

P How could you make a perfume from flower petals?
- What liquid would you use to dissolve the scent?
- What safety precautions would you take?

These cotton buds can be used to make cotton shirts

Linen, which is used in tablecloths and sheets, is made from the flax plant. Sisal fibres from the agave plant are used to make vacuum cleaner bags!

Plants give us dyes to colour these textiles.

The sisal fibres from these agave plants can be used to make vacuum cleaner bags

For example, the indigo plant gives a blue dye that can be used to colour denim.

Safflowers give an orange dye called carthamin.

Sphagnum moss contains a substance that kills germs. The moss used to be placed on wounds to help them heal. Aspirin originally came from the bark of willow trees.

Wood is used for building all kinds of things and for making paper. Paper is made from cellulose, the same substance that xylem tubes are made from. Tree trunks contain huge numbers of xylem tubes. The wood of Scots pine trees also gives us a paint stripper called turpentine.

Sphagnum moss

2 Write a list of all the plants mentioned on these pages. For each plant, say what it is used for.

3 Why is wood used to make paper?

4 Find out the names of some other plants that are used to produce medicines or dyes.

Willow tree

What are the differences between plant and animal cells?

Many things around us are made of smaller parts.
A building is made out of bricks, for instance. Living things are also made out of tiny parts, called **cells**. There are **animal cells** and **plant cells**. These cells are far too small to see, so we need to use **microscopes**. Our bodies contain over 1 000 000 000 000 animal cells!

The drawing below shows the parts of an animal cell. The photograph next to it shows a real animal cell. It is taken from the inside of somebody's cheek.

1 a) Name five living things that are made from animal cells.
b) Name five living things that are made from plant cells.

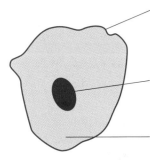

Cell membrane This is like a very thin bag. It keeps the cell together and controls what goes into and out of the cell.

Nucleus This is the 'control centre' of the cell. It tells that cell what to do.

Cytoplasm This is a jelly-like substance. Many of the cell's activities take place here.

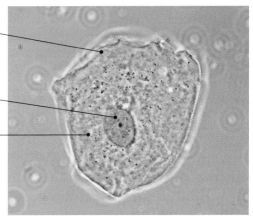

An animal cell (magnification ×2000)

2 a) What does the nucleus do?
b) What is the job of the cell membrane?
c) What happens in the cytoplasm?

Plant cells look a little different from animal cells, but they also have cytoplasm, a nucleus, and a cell membrane. Plant cells have straighter edges and are more box-shaped. These cells are from a moss leaf.

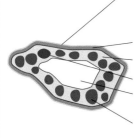

Cell wall This is like a box with many large holes in it. It supports the cell and is very strong. It is made out of a substance called **cellulose**.

Cell Membrane

Cytoplasm

Nucleus

Vacuole This is a storage space filled with a liquid called **cell sap**.

Chloroplasts These are green discs that allow the plant to make food (by **photosynthesis**). They contain a chemical called **chlorophyll**.

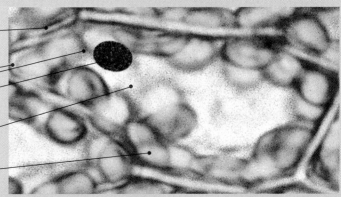

A plant cell (magnification ×2500)

3 a) Write down the cell parts that both plant and animal cells have.
   b) Write down the cell parts that plant cells have but animal cells do not.

4 What makes plant cells green?

To look at cells we need to use a microscope. Microscopes make things appear much bigger than they actually are. They **magnify** things.

The animal cell in the photograph on the opposite page is 2000 times bigger than in real life. It has been magnified 2000 times. We say it has a magnification of ×2000.

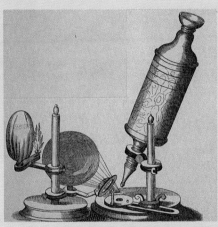
This microscope was used by Robert Hooke to see cells

This is a modern microscope that scientists use today

5 Measure the widest part of the cheek cell on the previous page. Now work out it's width in real life.

When using a microscope, we need to know what magnification we are using. Both the **eyepiece lens** and the **objective lens** do some magnifying. How much they each magnify is often written on the side of the lens. The total magnification we get is given by:

magnification of the eyepiece lens × magnification of the objective lens

An average animal cell is about 0.02 mm across. An average plant cell is about 0.04 mm across.

Cell membranes are only 0.00001 mm thick.

6 A microscope has a ×10 eyepiece lens and a ×15 objective lens. What is the total magnification?

7 a) Draw a basic line diagram of a plant cell and label all of its parts.
   b) Make a table to explain what each part of the plant cell does.

You should know…

- Animal cells have a nucleus, cytoplasm and a cell membrane.

- Plant cells also have a cell wall, a vacuole and chloroplasts.

- What all of these parts do.

Seeing is believing

How do we use a microscope?

To get a clear view of some cells, you need to use a microscope properly.

P

1 Place the smallest **objective lens** (the lowest **magnification**) over the hole in the stage.

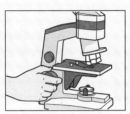

2 Turn the **coarse focusing wheel** to make the gap between the **stage** and the **objective lens** as small as possible.

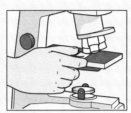

3 Place a **slide** under the clips on the **stage**.

4 Adjust the **light source** so that light goes up through the hole in the stage.

 Never point the mirror directly at the Sun. This can permanently damage your eyesight.

5 Look into the **eyepiece lens**.

6 Turn the **coarse focusing wheel** slowly until what you see is clear (**in focus**).

7 To see a bigger image, place the next largest **objective lens** over your **specimen**.

8 Use the **fine focusing wheel** to get your **image in focus** again. *Do not* use the coarse focusing wheel. You can break your slide and damage the microscope if you do. If you can't see anything, go back to a lower **magnification**.

1 A pupil sets up a microscope but can only see darkness when looking into the eyepiece lens. Write down what you think needs to be done to see the specimen.

2 Here is a set of five instructions on using the microscope. Write them in the correct order.
   A Look into the eyepiece lens.
   B Wind the coarse focusing wheel to focus.
   C Place the smallest objective lens over the hole in the stage.
   D Adjust the light source.
   E Place the slide under the clips on the stage.

3 Write down some rules of your own for:
   a) using a microscope safely   b) taking care of a microscope.

 In 1590 a spectacles maker from Holland called Zacharias Janssen placed two lenses into a tube and invented the microscope.

You should know...

● **The main parts of a microscope and what they do.**

How can we look at cells?

A **specimen** is the object that you look at under the microscope. The specimen needs to be thin so that light can pass through it. To make sure that a specimen is as thin as possible we flatten it out by putting it between a **slide** and a **coverslip**. Coverslips help to flatten out the specimen and also hold it in place and stop it drying out.

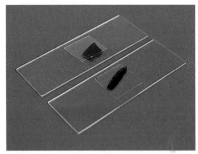

The specimen in the top slide is too thick

1 What is a specimen?

2 Why does a specimen need to be thin?

Slides and coverslips are made of thin glass. Be very careful when you are using them.

P You can look at some plant cells from an onion. Onions grow underground and so their cells do not have any chloroplasts, as they don't get any light.

Explain how you prepared your slide, including:
- any problems you had
- what sort of stain you used and why
- a labelled drawing of one or two of your cells.

1 Take a slide and place a drop of water in the centre. The water may contain a **stain** to make the cells show up better.

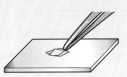

3 Place your onion skin onto the drop of water on your slide.

2 Using some forceps or your fingernails, peel off the inside layer of a piece of onion.

4 Using a mounted needle, lower a coverslip onto your onion skin. If you do this carefully and slowly you will not get any air bubbles.

3 Look at these two photographs:
   a) How can you tell that these are plant cells?
   b) Why do you think the cells in photograph B are clearer?
   c) What do you think the round ring labelled 'X' is?
   d) How can you avoid getting these round rings in your slides?

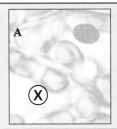 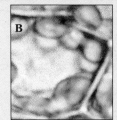

A   B   X

4 Why do we use coverslips?

5 a) What process happens in chloroplasts?
      Choose one of the following:
      A Reproduction   B Photosynthesis
      C Digestion   D Respiration
   b) Why don't onion cells have chloroplasts?

You should know…
- **How to prepare a microscope slide.**

23

Why do cells have different shapes?

Not all cells look the same. Some cells have a special shape to help them do a certain job.

Cells of the same type that are grouped together form a **tissue**. A tissue is a group of the same sort of cells, all working together to do a job. The group of muscle cells in the picture below is called **muscle tissue**.

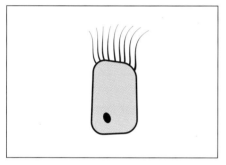

*A **ciliated epithelial** cell. The strands at the top (cilia) wave about to move things*

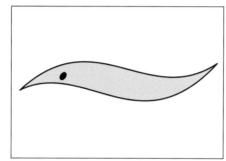

*A **muscle cell** is able to change length*

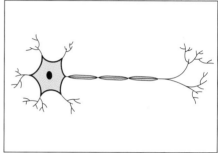

*A **nerve cell** is long so that messages can be carried around the body quickly (at speeds up to 300 km/h)*

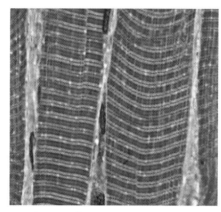

Ciliated epithelial tissue in a lung. The cilia wave together to move dirt out of the lungs. The cilia are killed off by cigarette smoke

Muscle tissue allows us to move

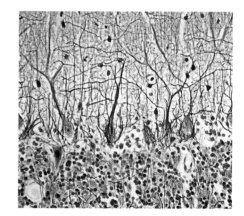

Nerve tissue in the brain

1 What is a tissue?

2 Why are nerve cells so long?

3 What does muscle tissue allow us to do?

4 Where would you expect to find a lot of nerve tissue?

An adult's body has over 200 types of cell. The longest are the nerve cells in the spine – these can be up to 1.3 m long. The smallest are another type of nerve cell found in the brain. These are only 0.005 mm long.

Not all the cells in a plant look the same.

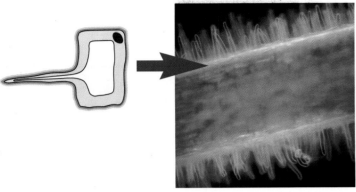

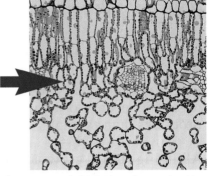

A **root hair cell** takes water out of the ground quickly. The root hair gives the water more surface to get into the cell

Root hair tissue

Palisade cells are packed with chloroplasts to help the plant make food

Palisade tissue forms a layer at the top of leaves

5 a) Which process, needing light, happens in palisade cells?
   b) Which part of the palisade cell does this process happen in?

6 a) What does a root hair cell do?
   b) How does the shape of a root hair cell help it to do this?
   c) Why are there no chloroplasts in a root hair cell?

Cells that have special shapes are said to be **adapted** to do certain jobs. The jobs that cells do, help us to live.

7 a) Explain how ciliated epithelial cells are adapted to remove dirt.
   b) What do you think happens to dirt in a smoker's lung?

8 Make labelled drawings of a ciliated epithelial cell and a root hair cell.

9 Look at this picture of a xylem cell.
   a) How are xylem cells adapted to carry water?
   b) What do you think a group of these cells is called?

This is a xylem cell from a plant stem. Xylem cells join together to form **xylem tubes**, which are hollow to carry water

In 1839 Theodor Schwann (1810–1882) said that cells were the smallest living units from which all plants and animals were made. Before this time, people thought that tissues were the smallest parts. They also thought that tissues were not living.

You should know...

- Some cells are adapted to do special jobs.

- How ciliated epithelial cells, nerve cells and root hair cells are adapted.

- A group of the same sort of cells is called a tissue.

How do cells help us to be alive?

For something to be alive it must move, reproduce, sense things, grow, respire, get rid of waste (excrete), and need nutrition. These are the seven 'life processes'. Cells do all of these things and so help us to carry out the seven life processes. For example, our nerve cells help us to sense things.

All living things grow. For whole plants and animals to get bigger, they need to make more cells. The cells need to reproduce. They do this by dividing. One cell divides to make two new cells. This is called **cell division**.

1 Which life processes do the following cells help us with:
a) nerve cells
b) muscle cells?

2 a) What is cell division?
b) Which life process does cell division help with?

The nucleus of the cell splits into two.

A new cell membrane forms in the middle.

The new **daughter cells** get bigger.

Once the **daughter cells** are full size, they too can divide.

When a cell divides, the two new cells are called **daughter cells**. The daughter cells made by cell division are quite small. Before they can divide they must grow to full size. To do this they require nutrition. Our cells get nutrition from the food we eat. That is why people who do not get enough food may not grow as tall as they should.

3 Look at this photograph:
a) Which cell is dividing (A, B or C)?
b) How can you tell?
c) Make a drawing of the dividing cell and label the parts.

4 Draw a diagram to show how cells divide.

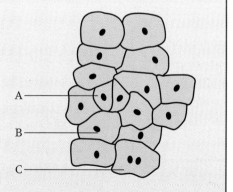

A

B

C

Sometimes cell division goes wrong and cells start to divide faster than they should. Cancer cells do this.

a cancer tumour

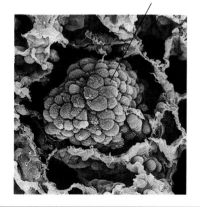

26

B2d Organs

What is an organ?

Cells of the same type are grouped together to form tissues. Different types of tissues can be grouped together to make **organs**. Organs carry out very important jobs.

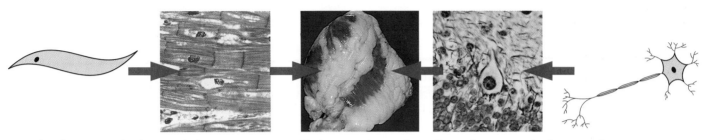

Muscle cells are grouped to form muscle tissue

The heart contains muscle and nerve tissues

Nerve cells are grouped to form nerve tissue

 1 Name two tissues found in the heart.

The heart is an organ. It is made of muscle tissue and nerve tissue, as well as some other tissues such as fat tissue. The heart has a very important job to do. It pumps blood around the body to supply all of our cells with food and oxygen.

 2 What job does the heart do?

Plants have organs too.

Root hair cells are grouped to form root hair tissue

The root contains root hair and xylem tissues.

Xylem cells are grouped to form xylem tissue
The xylem tissue has been stained so that you can see where it is

The root is an organ. It is made of root hair tissue and xylem tissue, as well as some other plant tissues. Its job is to take water out of the ground so that the plant can use it. The root hair tissue takes water out of the ground and the xylem tissue carries it to the stem. The stem can then take the water to the leaves.

3 Name two tissues found in the root.

4 What job does the root do?

5 Name another organ found in plants.

6 Name one sort of tissue that might be found in a plant stem.

You should know...

● **Different tissues are grouped together to form organs.**

● **Each organ has a very important job**

27

What do human organs do?

There are many organs inside our bodies. Each one has a very important job to do.

1 Write down the names of five organs in the body

The brain is the most important organ in our bodies. It controls the body and makes sure that it works properly. The human brain is divided into two halves and each half has a different responsibility. The right-hand side controls imagination, and artistic and musical talent. The left-hand side controls memory, speaking, reading, writing and mathematical ability.

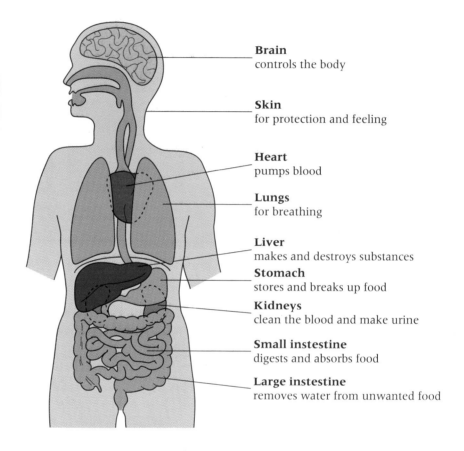

Brain
controls the body

Skin
for protection and feeling

Heart
pumps blood

Lungs
for breathing

Liver
makes and destroys substances

Stomach
stores and breaks up food

Kidneys
clean the blood and make urine

Small instestine
digests and absorbs food

Large instestine
removes water from unwanted food

2 Using the organs you chose in Question 1, copy and complete the following table.

Organ	What it does

3 a) Which organ makes urine?   b) Which organ takes in air?
c) Name three organs that food passes through.

4 Name one sort of tissue you might find in the brain.

5 Write a report about the heart. You should include where it is, what it is made of and what it does. Try to find out how a doctor listens for it.

6 Try to find out more about one other organ in the body.

You should know...

● **About all the organs on this page, where they are and what they do.**

What do plant organs do?

There are four main organs found in plants.

Flower
— holds the reproductive parts and so produces seeds

Stem
carries substances around the plant. It has a lot of xylem tissue to help it carry water. It also holds the leaves in place

Leaf
makes food by the process of photosynthesis

Root
takes water out of the ground with the help of root hairs. It also holds the plant in the ground

 1 a) In which organ does photosynthesis take place?
   b) Which organ contains root hair tissue?
   c) Which organ contains the most xylem tissue?
   d) Which organ is used for plant reproduction?

Photosynthesis is the process that plants use to make food. It takes place in the leaves when there is light. Photosynthesis needs water (from the ground) and carbon dioxide (from the air). The food that is made is **sugar**. Oxygen is also made.

 Plant leaves are organs that are designed to collect sunlight. The more area they can cover, the more sunlight they can collect. The biggest leaf ever found was from an Alocasia plant in Malaysia. It was 3 m long and nearly 2 m wide.

 2 In which organ are seeds produced?

3 a) Write down two substances needed for photosynthesis.
   b) Which of these substances is a liquid?
   c) Through which organ does this liquid enter the plant?
   d) Through which organ does this liquid go through to reach the leaves?
   e) Which tissue in these organs does the water travel in?

4 a) Write down the substances made by photosynthesis.
   b) Which of these substances does the plant use for food?

You should know...

● About all the plant organs on this page, where they are and what they do.

● Plants make their own food using photosynthesis.

● Photosynthesis needs light to work.

● Photosynthesis uses up water and carbon dioixde and makes sugar and oxygen.

How do organs work together?

In plants, the water needed for photosynthesis comes from the soil. It travels through a series of organs on its way to the leaf. The root, stem and leaf form a **water transport system**. This is an example of organs working together. A set of organs working together is called an **organ system**.

Not all of the water that reaches a leaf is used for photosynthesis. Some of the water comes out of the surface of the leaf and goes into the air.

 1 Which weather conditions do you think make leaves lose the most water? Choose from the following and explain your choice:
A Windy and cold   B Still and cold
C Windy and hot   D Still and hot

*The **water transport system** in plants contains three organs – root, stem and leaves*

 Plan an investigation to find out which conditions make leaves lose water fastest.
- Which conditions will you use?
- How will you find out how much water has been lost?
- How will you make it a fair test?
- Which conditions do you predict will cause the water to be lost the fastest?

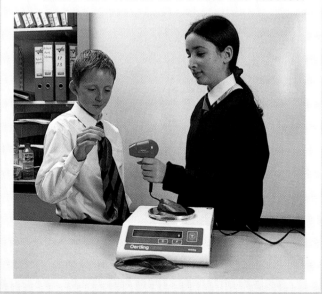

We have organ systems in our bodies. Two of the important ones are the **digestive system** and the **breathing system**.

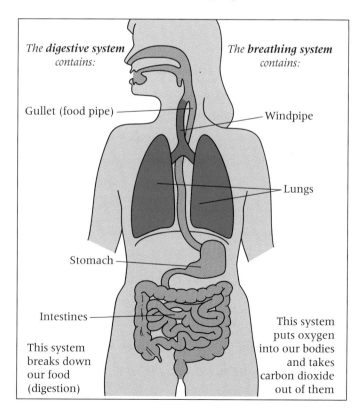

*The **digestive system** contains:*

Gullet (food pipe)

Stomach

Intestines

This system breaks down our food (digestion)

*The **breathing system** contains:*

Windpipe

Lungs

This system puts oxygen into our bodies and takes carbon dioxide out of them

2 Write down the names of the organs in each of these organ systems:
  a) the digestive system
  b) the breathing system.

3 Write down the jobs that each of these organ systems do:
  a) the digestive system
  b) the breathing system.

There are other important organ systems in our bodies.

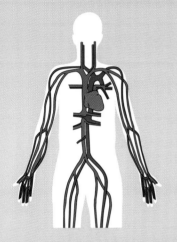

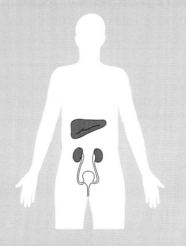

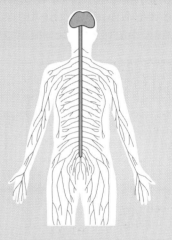

The **circulatory system** *contains the heart and the blood vessels. It carries oxygen and food around the body*

The **excretory system** *contains the kidneys, bladder and liver. It gets rid of poisonous waste from the body*

The **nervous system** *contains the brain and spinal cord. It carries messages around the body*

The circulatory system contains over 100 000 km of blood vessels carrying blood.

The excretory system is very efficient. All of your blood is cleaned every five minutes by the kidneys. The urine that is made is stored in the bladder.

4 Make a table with five columns, one for each of the human organ systems on these pages. Fill in the organs that each organ system contains.

5 Research one of the organ systems above, and write a short report about it.

You should know ...

- Cells group to form tissues. Tissues group to form organs. Organs group to form organ systems. All of these make up a living thing – an organism.

- Water is lost by plants through their leaves.

- The organs in the breathing and digestive systems.

- What the breathing and digestive systems do.

How do plants reproduce?

Living things don't last for ever and so new ones must replace those that die. New living things are produced by **reproduction**. Plants can reproduce in two ways: **sexual reproduction** and **asexual reproduction**.

Sexual reproduction needs a male and a female. The male and female parts of a plant are called **reproductive organs** and are found in the flowers. Most plants have the male and female parts in the same flower.

Prospero Alpino (1553–1616) was the first person to realise that plants had male and female parts. He also introduced coffee and bananas to Europe.

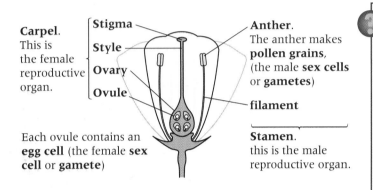

Carpel. This is the female reproductive organ.

Stigma
Style
Ovary
Ovule

Anther. The anther makes **pollen grains**, (the male **sex cells** or **gametes**)

filament

Stamen. this is the male reproductive organ.

Each ovule contains an **egg cell** (the female **sex cell** or **gamete**)

1 a) Name the male reproductive organ of a plant.
   b) List its parts.
   c) A pollen grain is a cell. Which part of the cell controls it?

2 a) Name the female reproductive organ of a plant.
   b) List its parts.
   c) What is the female gamete called?

In **sexual reproduction**, the **nucleus** from the pollen grain of one plant joins with the nucleus from the egg cell of another plant. The new nucleus contains all the information needed to make the new plant. Half of this information has come from one plant and the other half from another plant. The new plant will have some features from both plants.

The advantage of sexual reproduction is that it mixes features and produces new **varieties** of plant.

You should know...

- **Sexual reproduction needs male and female sex cells (gametes) to join.**
- **Sexual reproduction produces new varieties.**
- **The parts of the flower and where the sex cells are made.**

3 a) Which feature of Plant C came from Plant A?
   b) Which feature of Plant C came from Plant B?

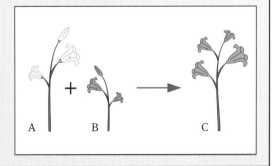

A   B   C

Asexual reproduction

How do plants reproduce without using flowers?

Many plants reproduce asexually. **Asexual reproduction** does not need sex cells. Instead, a part of the parent plant forms a new plant.

runner

For example, strawberries grow **runners**. These spread over the ground and sprout roots at intervals. Once the new plants have opened their leaves and can photosynthesise, the runner rots away.

Potato plants send out many underground stems. These swell up at the ends and form potato **tubers** ('potatoes'). They contain a store of food (starch). Each potato tuber can grow into a new potato plant.

 1 a) Describe two methods by which plants reproduce asexually.
   b) Give an example of a plant that uses each method.

Gardeners use asexual reproduction to produce *identical* new plants quickly and cheaply. They cut off a side stem from a plant and place it in moist soil. Eventually the stem sprouts roots and forms a new plant, which is exactly the same as the parent plant. This is called 'taking a cutting'.

New plants made by asexual reproduction are all exactly the same as the parent plant. Asexual reproduction does not produce new **varieties** but it is much faster than sexual reproduction.

 Some plants, like Kalanchoe, produce new little plants on their leaves.

 2 a) What does 'taking a cutting' mean?
   b) What are the advantages for gardeners of this method of reproduction?

 Some new plants can sprout from cuts made in leaves. How could you investigate the best place to make a cut in a Begonia leaf to grow a new plant?
   • Where will you make the different cuts?
   • Where will you put your cut leaf?

 3 What are the advantages and disadvantages of:
   a) sexual reproduction
   b) asexual reproduction?

How does pollen get from one plant to another?

Sexual reproduction in plants produces seeds. The first step in making a seed takes place when pollen from the anther of one flower gets to the stigma of another. This is called **pollination**.

First, the anther splits open to allow the pollen to escape. The pollen can then be carried away from the anther by:
- insects
- the wind.

The anther on the stamen splits open to reveal the pollen grains.

1 What is pollination?

2 Name two ways in which pollen can be carried from flower to flower.

Insect pollination

Buttercups, poppies, daisies and dandelions are all flowers that need insects to carry their pollen. Insect-pollinated flowers have special features to help with reproduction.

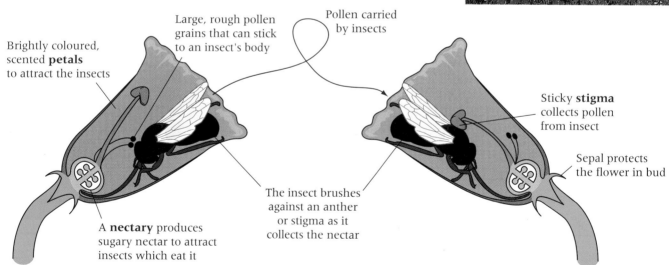

Brightly coloured, scented **petals** to attract the insects

Large, rough pollen grains that can stick to an insect's body

Pollen carried by insects

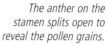

Sticky **stigma** collects pollen from insect

Sepal protects the flower in bud

The insect brushes against an anther or stigma as it collects the nectar

A **nectary** produces sugary nectar to attract insects which eat it

Insect pollination of a foxglove

Bees need to collect nectar from about 2 million flowers to make 0.5 kg of honey.

3 How do flowers attract insects?

4 What do insects collect from flowers?

Wind pollination

Hazel trees and grasses use the wind to spread their pollen from flower to flower. Wind-pollinated flowers have different features from insect-pollinated flowers.

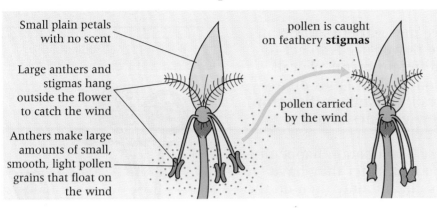

Small plain petals with no scent

Large anthers and stigmas hang outside the flower to catch the wind

Anthers make large amounts of small, smooth, light pollen grains that float on the wind

pollen is caught on feathery **stigmas**

pollen carried by the wind

Wind pollination of rye grass

Hazel catkins produce large amounts of small pollen grains

5   Name two plants that are wind pollinated.

6   Name three plants that are insect pollinated.

7   Why are pollen grains from wind-pollinated flowers small and light?

8   Why do the anthers and stigmas of a wind-pollinated plant hang outside the flower?

9   a) Look at these pictures of the pollen grains. Which one is from an insect-pollinated flower? Explain your reasoning.

b) Work out how big these pollen grains are in real life.

Magnified 202 times

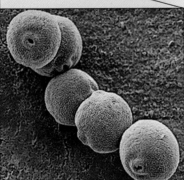

Magnified 3156 times

Can you see the differences between pollen carried on the wind and pollen carried by insects?
- What equipment will you need?
- What will you need to do?
- What will you look for?

Pollen from wind-pollinated plants causes some people to get hayfever. In the summer the number of pollen grains in the air can reach up to 3000 grains per cubic metre.

You should know...

● Pollination is the transfer of pollen from anther to stigma.

● Flowering plants can be wind pollinated or insect pollinated.

● The difference between wind and insect pollinated flowers.

Plant crossing

What are cross-pollination and self-pollination?

Sexual reproduction should produce new varieties of plant. For this to happen, pollen from one flower needs to get to the stigma of another flower on a different plant. We call this **cross-pollination**. If pollen from a plant lands on a stigma of the same plant, then we call this **self-pollination**. Self-pollination will not produce new varieties of plant.

Plants use one of two ways to stop self-pollination happening. In most plants the anthers split open first. After they have released all their pollen, the anthers die and only then do the stigmas become mature and ready to receive pollen.

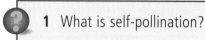

1 What is self-pollination?

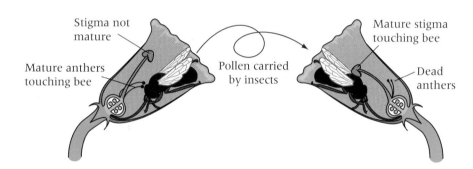

Stigma not mature

Mature anthers touching bee

Pollen carried by insects

Mature stigma touching bee

Dead anthers

Some plants use a different method to make sure cross-pollination happens. The plants have only male reproductive organs or female reproductive organs. For example, holly trees either have male flowers or female flowers.

2 a) What is cross-pollination?
  b) Describe two ways of making sure that cross-pollination happens.

Only female holly trees wil produce berries

Scientists often want to produce new varieties of plant. They take pollen from one plant and put it onto the stigmas of another plant. To stop self-pollination happening, all the anthers from the second plant are removed. Producing new varieties in this way is called **plant crossing**.

3 After putting pollen from one flower onto the flowers of another plant, scientists often wrap the flowers in clear plastic bags and wait for the seeds to grow:
  a) What part of a flower do they get the pollen from?
  b) What part of a flower do they put the pollen onto?
  c) Why do you think they use the plastic bags?

Which other animals can pollinate plants?

An animal that pollinates a plant is called a **pollinator**. Most pollinators are insects, which are attracted by a plant's flowers. Many insects feed on nectar. The brightly coloured petals and the smell of the flowers helps to guide the insect to where the nectar is, so that pollen can be placed onto the insect or brushed off it.

Some flowers do not provide any nectar and attract insects in other ways. For example, Deadhorse Arum flowers give off the smell of rotting flesh and have flowers that, to flies, look like dead animals.

One of the biggest flowers in the world belongs to a tropical plant called the Titan Arum. Its flowers can grow up to 3 m tall and 1 m across. It gives off a smell like rotting fish, which attracts small bees.

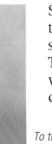
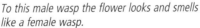

Some orchids make themselves look and smell like female insects. The male insects try to mate with the flowers and get covered in pollen.

To this male wasp the flower looks and smells like a female wasp.

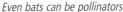

Insects are not the only pollinators. Around the world, many birds, mammals and reptiles are used by plants to take pollen from one plant to another.

Even bats can be pollinators

 Flowers that are pollinated by birds do not have a smell because most birds cannot smell.

1 Why are flies attracted to Arum plants? Explain in as much detail as you can.

2 How do some orchids attract pollinators?

3 What might pollen stick to on a mammal pollinator?

4 Some flowers only open at night. What does this tell you about the pollinator?

How does pollination lead to the formation of a seed?

Once a pollen grain has landed on a stigma, a **pollen tube** begins to grow. The stigma makes a sugar solution to help the pollen tube grow down the style to the ovary. Eventually it reaches an ovule. The nucleus from the pollen grain goes down the tube and into the egg cell, found inside in the ovule.

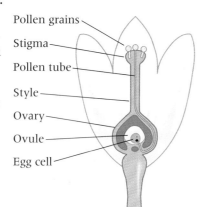

Pollen grains
Stigma
Pollen tube
Style
Ovary
Ovule
Egg cell

P What strength of sugar solution do pollen tubes grow best in?
- How would you look at pollen tubes?
- How many different strengths of sugar solution would you use?
- What do you think would happen?

 1 How does the nucleus from a pollen grain get to the egg cell?

The pollen grain nucleus joins with the egg cell nucleus to form a **zygote**. This is called **fertilisation**. Fertilisation can only occur between plants of the same type (**species**). After this, the flower dies. The zygote turns into an embryo, which has a tiny root and a tiny shoot. The ovule becomes the seed with a hard outer **seed coat**. The ovary swells up and becomes the **fruit** around the seed.

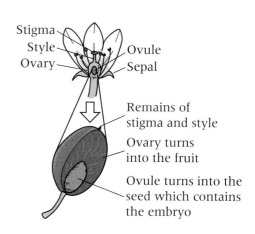

Stigma
Style
Ovary
Ovule
Sepal
Remains of stigma and style
Ovary turns into the fruit
Ovule turns into the seed which contains the embryo

 2 a) Explain what is meant by the word 'fertilisation'.
  b) What is a zygote?
  c) What does a zygote turn into?

3 What happens to the flower after fertilisation?

4 What do the ovule and ovary turn into after fertilisation?

5 What do fruits contain?

 The largest seed in the world is the double coconut seed, which can have a mass of up to 20 kg.

You should know...

- What pollen tubes are.
- Fertilisation is the joining of a nucleus from a male sex cell with one from a female sex cell.
- In fertilisation, a zygote is formed. This turns into an embryo.
- Which parts of the flower become which parts of the fruit.

B3c Spreading seeds

How are seeds spread away from the parent plants?

Seeds need to be spread away from the parent plant. This is called **seed dispersal** and the fruit helps this to happen. There are two types of fruit: fleshy and dry fruits.

Fleshy fruits are soft, juicy and good to eat. They are often brightly coloured to attract animals to eat them. Tomatoes and plums are examples of fleshy fruits.

The flesh of the fruit is easily digested. The seeds are protected by the tough **seed coat** and pass through the animal, ending up in the animal's droppings.

 Eating fruit gives animals (and us) energy and vitamins. Avocado fruits contain the most chemical energy of any fruit (781 kJ/100 g). They also contain vitamins A and C.

 1 Why are the seeds inside fleshy fruits not digested?

 Karl von Nägeli (1817–1891) was the first scientist to understand why seeds need to be spread to prevent competition between the parent plants and seedlings.

Dry fruits use animals, wind, water and even explosions to disperse their seeds.

Burdock fruits have hooks. They attach themselves to animal fur and are carried by the animals before falling off

Lupin fruits explode, scattering the seeds inside over a wide area

Coconut fruits are carried by the sea

Dandelion fruits are carried by the wind

 2 Why do you think coconut palm trees are naturally only found on beaches?

Dispersal of seeds is important. It allows the new plants to grow in new areas away from the parent plants. The new plants can get light, space, water and nutrients without competition from the parent plants.

 3 a) What does the word 'dispersal' mean?
b) Why is it important?
c) List all the ways in which seeds can be dispersed.

4 Why do you think tomato plants are common around sewage works?

You should know...
- **Fruits are either fleshy or dry.**
- **Fruits help to disperse seeds using animals, wind, water and explosions.**
- **Seeds are dispersed to stop them competing with the parent plants.**

How do seeds grow into plants?

Seeds usually look dry and dead. However, they contain everything needed to grow into new plants. A seed starts to grow when it is given the right conditions. This is called **germination**.

 Seeds can wait a long time before conditions are right to grow. In 1966 some Canadian scientists managed to germinate seeds found in some frozen soil. They were nearly 15 000 years old!

 1 a) What is germination?
b) Write down a list of things that you think seeds might need so they can germinate.

The seed is surrounded by a hard, tough **seed coat**. Inside this coat is the **embryo**. There is also a store of food. For the seed to germinate it needs water, oxygen and warmth. When it germinates, the seed coat breaks open and the root of the embryo starts to grow. Soon after this, the shoot starts to grow.

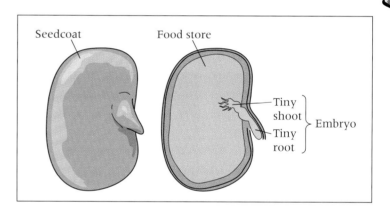

Seedcoat   Food store

Tiny shoot
Tiny root
} Embryo

P If you plant seeds upside down, do the roots grow upwards?
- What equipment would you use?
- What conditions would your seeds need?
- What do you think would happen?

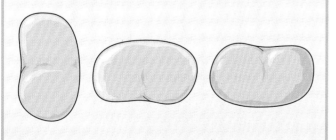

 2 Why is the seed coat hard and tough?

3 Why does the seed need a store of food?

4 Seeds don't need light to germinate. Why do you think this is?

You should know...
- **Germination is when a seed starts to grow.**
- **Germination requires water, oxygen and warmth (WOW!).**

How do plants make food?

When a seed germinates, the root emerges first. The root absorbs water from the ground and holds the seed in place. As it grows, the food store shrivels. The first green leaves open and the young plant is now called a **seedling**.

 1 Why do you think the root grows first?

Once a plant has some leaves it can make its own food using photosynthesis. To do this, energy is needed. The energy used is the light energy from the Sun.

 2 Why doesn't photosynthesis happen in the dark?

Light energy is trapped by the **chloroplasts**. These contain a green substance, called **chlorophyll**, to help them trap the light. Using the light energy, the chloroplasts turn the raw materials carbon dioxide and water into sugar and oxygen. A lot of the oxygen is let back into the air. The sugar is the plant's food. A lot of this sugar is stored in the plant as **starch**.

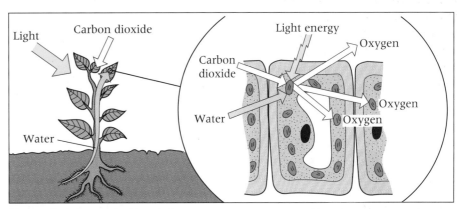

Photosynthesis happens in chloroplasts

 3 Which gas, produced by plants, is useful for humans?

4 a) Name the raw materials for photosynthesis.
b) Name the products of photosynthesis.

5 Which parts of a plant cell trap light energy from the Sun?

6 How does a plant store its food?

You should know...

● **In germination, the root grows first, then the shoot.**

● **When the first leaves open the young plant is called a seedling.**

● **Plants use their leaves to make food using photosynthesis. Carbon dioxide and water are changed into sugar and oxygen using light energy.**

Why do plants need various things to grow well?

To grow well a plant needs: light, air (carbon dioxide and oxygen), water, warmth and nutrients.

Photosynthesis needs light. Plants grown without light become tall, thin and yellow. A plant like this will die quite quickly.

This is a healthy plant   This plant has not had enough light

Photosynthesis also needs carbon dioxide and water to make sugar. The sugar is used to make new substances that the plant needs to grow. The sugar is also used to provide energy.

Respiration is the process that releases energy. All the cells of a plant need to **respire** to get energy. Oxygen and sugar are used up in respiration and carbon dioxide and water are produced. *Photosynthesis* only occurs during the day. *Respiration* happens all the time.

?
1 Write down two ways that sugar is used in a plant.

2 a) Which process releases energy in plants?
   b) Where does this process occur?
   c) When does it occur?

Plants also use water to help support themselves. A plant with too little water starts to droop or **wilt**.

Plants need to be warm to grow well. Most plants will not grow if the temperature is below 5 °C or above 45 °C.

Plants also need nutrients from the soil, called **mineral salts**. The important ones are chemicals containing nitrogen, phosphorus and potassium. Fertilisers contain these chemicals. Mineral salts that contain nitrogen are called **nitrates**. Nitrates are used by the plant to make sugar into proteins, which are used for growth. Plants grow very badly without nitrates.

The plant on the left was grown without nitrates in the soil. The other plant had nitrates in the soil

?
3 What has happened to a plant that has wilted?

4 What are mineral salts?

5 Why are nitrates so important?

You should know...

● For a plant to grow well it needs light, air, water, warmth and nutrients (LAWWN).

● Why each of these is needed.

● Respiration releases energy in all the cells of a plant.

● Nitrates are used by the plant to make sugar into proteins.

Plant ingredients

How do plants obtain the things that they need?

Light

Plant leaves contain **palisade cells**, packed with green chloroplasts that absorb light. Leaves are much paler green on the underside. The cells there contain fewer chloroplasts. Many leaves have a big surface area to help them get as much sunlight as possible.

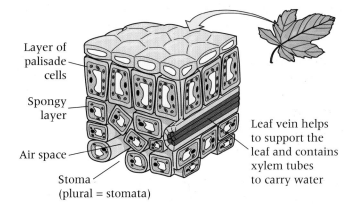

Layer of palisade cells

Spongy layer

Air space

Stoma (plural = stomata)

Leaf vein helps to support the leaf and contains xylem tubes to carry water

 1 Why are the undersides of leaves a paler green than the tops?

Air

Carbon dioxide from the air enters the leaves through small holes on the underside of leaves, called **stomata**. Most leaves are thin so that the carbon dioxide does not have far to go before reaching a cell that needs it. Oxygen for respiration can also enter through these holes.

 2 What are stomata?

3 At night the air spaces in a leaf fill up with carbon dioxide. Why do you think this is?

Water

Water is obtained by the roots. Roots have **root hair cells**. These absorb a lot of water. The water is passed from cell to cell until it reaches a xylem tube. **Xylem tubes** carry water to the leaves.

 Some plants can heat themselves up! The skunk cabbage is able to increase its temperature by about 9 °C and melt the snow around it.

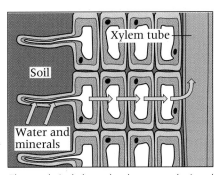

Xylem tube

Soil

Water and minerals

Warmth

Most plants stop growing when it gets too cold.

Nutrients

Plants absorb **mineral salts**, dissolved in water, through their roots.

The root hairs help to absorb water and mineral salts from the soil

 4 Make a drawing of a palisade cell and say how its structure helps it to do its job.

5 Make a drawing of a root hair cell and say how its structure helps it to do its job.

6 Why do gardeners and farmers add fertiliser to the soil?

7 How do mineral salts get to the leaves of a plant?

You should know...
- **How a plant obtains light, air, water and nutrients.**

What happens during puberty and adolescence?

Between the ages of ten and fifteen, physical changes start to happen in our bodies. These changes continue until the age of about eighteen. The time when these physical changes happen is called **puberty**. Girls usually start puberty before boys.

Puberty is controlled by chemicals called **sex hormones** that are released in our bodies. In girls, puberty starts when the **ovaries** start to produce sex hormones.

1 What is puberty?

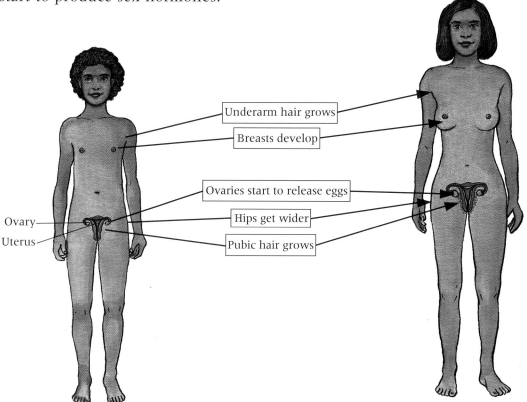

Underarm hair grows

Breasts develop

Ovary

Uterus

Ovaries start to release eggs

Hips get wider

Pubic hair grows

2 Make a list of all the changes that happen to a girl's body during puberty.

3 What controls puberty?

An animal is said to have reached sexual maturity when it can reproduce. This varies from species to species:
   Human 12–15 years
   Elephant 10–13 years
   Salmon 5 years
   Turtle 3 years
   Kangaroo 2 years
   Mouse 35 days

In boys, puberty starts when the **testes** start to produce a sex hormone.

4 Make a list of all the changes that happen to a boy's body during puberty.

5 Where are the sex hormones made in:
   a) a girl
   b) a boy?

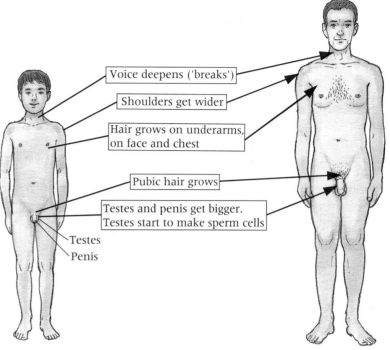

Voice deepens ('breaks')

Shoulders get wider

Hair grows on underarms, on face and chest

Pubic hair grows

Testes and penis get bigger. Testes start to make sperm cells

Testes
Penis

Emotional changes also occur, as well as physical changes. The time when all these emotional and physical changes occur is called **adolescence**.

Sex hormones make boys and girls become more interested in each other. The hormones may also cause mood swings. Friends and family, and 'agony aunts' in newspapers and magazines, are all there to offer help and support.

Sex hormones can also be responsible for causing spots (**acne**).

In medieval times, choirboys sometimes had their testes cut off (castration) before they reached puberty. This prevented their voices 'breaking'.

6 What is adolescence?

7 Make a list of the physical changes that happen to both boys and girls.

8 What do we mean by 'emotional changes'?

9 a) What is acne?
   b) Imagine you work on an advice column in a magazine. Somebody writes to you saying that they have terrible acne. What advice would you give them?

You should know...

● Puberty describes the time when physical changes happen.

● Both physical and emotional changes occur during adolescence.

● The changes start between the ages of ten and fifteen and end at about eighteen.

What do the parts of the human reproductive system do?

Sexual reproduction needs a male **sex cell** to join with a female sex cell. The **reproductive organs** produce the sex cells (**gametes**) and allow sexual reproduction to take place. The reproductive organs form an organ system called the **reproductive system**.

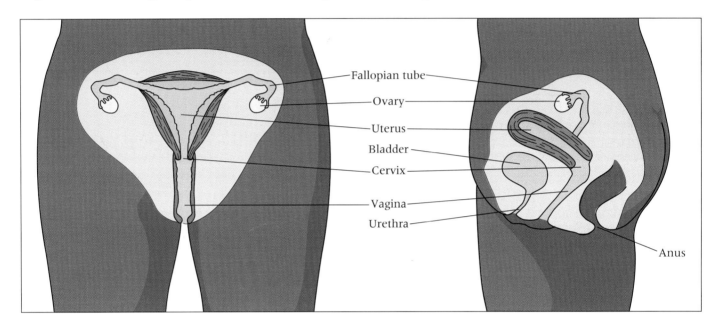

The female sex cells (female **gametes**) are the **egg cells**. The ovaries contain hundreds of small, undeveloped egg cells. Once every 28–31 days, an egg cell from one of the ovaries becomes mature and is released into the **fallopian tube** (sometimes called the oviduct or egg tube).

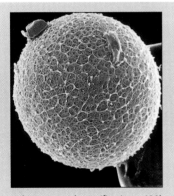

A human egg (magnification ×420)

1 a) What are the female gametes called?
b) Where are they released from?

The fallopian tube is lined with small hairs (**cilia**) which move the egg cell slowly along the tube towards the **uterus** (womb). The uterus is where the baby will develop. It has strong, muscular walls and a soft lining.

2 How does an egg cell get to the uterus?

3 What is the cervix?

The lower end of the uterus is made of a ring of muscle called the **cervix**. The cervix holds the baby in place during pregnancy. The cervix opens into the **vagina**.

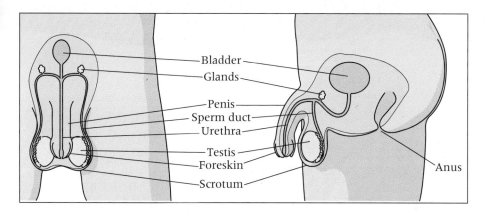

The male sex cells (male **gametes**) are the **sperm cells**. They are made in the testes. The testes are held outside the body in a bag of skin called the **scrotum**. Their position helps to keep the sperm cells at the right temperature to develop properly.

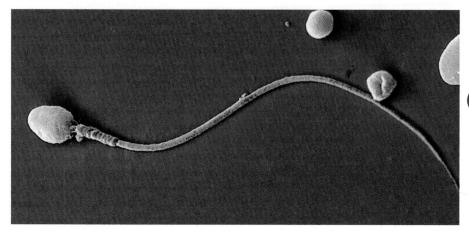

A human sperm cell (magnification ×4000)

When sperm cells are released from the testes they travel up the **sperm ducts**, where special fluids are added from **glands**. The fluids give the sperm cells energy. Together the sperm cells and the fluids are called **semen**. The semen flows through a tube running down the centre of the penis called the **urethra**. The urethra also carries urine from the bladder, but never at the same time as semen.

The head of the penis is sensitive and is protected by a covering of skin (the **foreskin**). This is sometimes removed for religious reasons or because it is too tight. This is called **circumcision**.

After puberty, a man will produce sperm for the rest of his life. The ovaries in women stop releasing egg cells at about the age of 45–55. The time when this happens is called the **menopause**.

4 a) Where are sperm cells made?
   b) Do you think sperm cells like to be warmer or colder than the body?

5 What is semen?

6 What substances can the urethra carry?

Adult men produce up to 100 million sperm cells every day.

You should know...

- **The parts and jobs of the male and female reproductive organs.**

- **Sperm cells (from the testes) and egg cells (from the ovaries) are the human sex cells (gametes).**

- **Egg cells stop being released in females at the menopause.**

7 If a woman released an egg cell every 28 days for 35 years of her life, how many egg cells would she release in total? Show your working.

8 What is circumcision?

9 What is the menopause?

What is the menstrual cycle?

In **menstruation** the soft lining of the uterus breaks apart. It passes out of the vagina along with a little blood. Another term used for menstruation is 'having a period'. A 'period' usually lasts for 3–7 days.

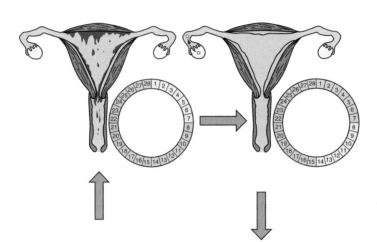

About 14 days after ovulation, if the egg has not been fertilised by a sperm cell, the lining of the uterus breaks apart again. The cycle starts again with another 'period'.

Immediately after menstruation, an egg cell starts to mature in one of the ovaries. While this happens, the soft lining of the uterus starts to build up. About 14 days after the cycle has started, the egg cell is released. This is **ovulation**.

The egg cell is swept along the fallopian tube towards the uterus. If the egg cell meets a sperm cell it will be **fertilised**. The soft lining of the uterus is able to feed a fertilised egg cell. The lining is replaced each cycle to make sure it can do this. It continues to thicken for about a week after ovulation.

*The **menstrual cycle**, lasting 28–32 days, is a series of events that occur in the female reproductive system*

'Periods' usually occur once every 28–31 days, but this can vary quite a lot, especially when periods first start. Sanitary towels or tampons are used to absorb the blood.

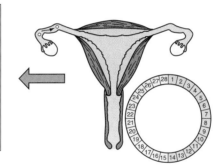

1 How long does one complete cycle of the menstrual cycle take?

2 a) What happens during menstruation (a 'period')?
b) How long does menstruation last?

3 What happens about 14 days after menstruation starts?

4 Why does the soft uterus lining have to become thick?

You should know...

● **The menstrual cycle lasts about 28 days. It begins with menstruation.**

● **Ovulation (release of an egg cell) occurs in the middle of the cycle.**

How are sperm and egg cells adapted for the jobs that they do?

Sperm cells are the male gametes. They are extremely small. Each one is only about 0.06 mm long. 170 sperm cells, end to end, would only measure 1 cm.

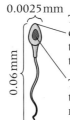

0.0025 mm

The tip of the head contains chemicals which attack the coat of the egg, helping the sperm to burrow inside

The nucleus contains half the instructions needed to make a new human

0.06 mm

The tail helps it to swim well

1 Which part of a sperm cell helps it to reach the egg?

2 Which part of the sperm cell helps it to burrow into the egg?

Egg cells are the female gametes. They are often called eggs or ova (singular: ovum). The egg cell is much bigger than the sperm cell. Egg cells are about 0.1 mm wide.

Walther Flemming (1843–1905) was one of the first scientists to use stains to see things better under the microscope. Using his stains, he discovered chromosomes.

Egg cells and sperm cells contain nuclei. Each nucleus has 23 thread-like pieces inside it called **chromosomes**. Each set of 23 chromosomes contains half the instructions for a new human life.

In fertilisation the sperm cell joins with the egg cell to form a fertilised egg cell called a **zygote**. The nucleus in the zygote contains a full set of 46 chromosomes. Every nucleus in human cells (apart from sperm and egg cells) contains 46 chromosomes arranged in pairs.

0.1 mm *smaller than a full stop.*

The cytoplasm contains a store food used to provide energy for the zygote to develop

The nucleus contains half the instructions needed to make a new human

The jelly coat helps to make sure that only one sperm can enter

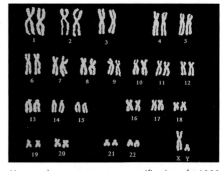

Human chromosomes at a magnification of ×1000

3 Where does the developing fertilised egg cell get its energy from?

4 How many chromosomes does the nucleus of a human nerve cell contain?

5 a) What are chromosomes?
b) Where are they found?

6 What feature do both egg cells and sperm cells have?

7 Draw a picture of a sperm cell and an egg cell. Label the parts that help each to do its job.

You should know...

- **The nucleus of almost every human cell has 23 pairs of chromosomes (46 altogether).**

- **Gametes only have 23 chromosomes.**

- **Sperm cells have tails to swim and chemicals in their heads.**

- **Egg cells contain a store of food and have a jelly coat.**

How does sexual intercourse produce a baby?

There are many forms of love. A special love between a man and a woman can lead to marriage. Men and women often show that they love each other by having sexual intercourse, also called 'having sex' or 'making love'.

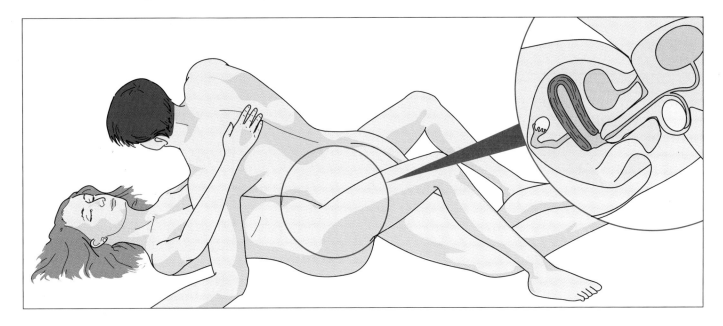

Before sex, the woman becomes excited and her vagina becomes moist. The man also becomes excited and his penis fills with blood. This makes the penis stiff and erect (an **erection**). The penis is inserted into the vagina and the man moves it backwards and forwards. Eventually semen is pumped out into the top of the vagina. This is called **ejaculation**.

> **?** **1** What fills the penis to make it stiff and erect?
>
> **2** What is ejaculation?

The semen is sucked up through the cervix. Small movements of the uterus wall carry it up to the fallopian tubes. Here, the sperm cells start to swim up the fallopian tubes. If a sperm cell meets an egg in a fallopian tube, the sperm burrows into it and **fertilises** it.

> **?** **3** What is fertilisation?

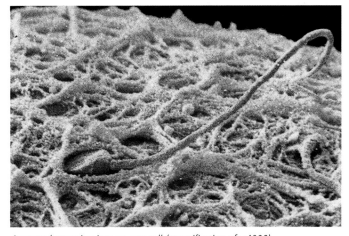

A sperm burrowing into an egg cell (magnification of ×4000)

The fertilised egg cell (**zygote**) divides into two. Each of these cells then divides into two again. The cells carry on dividing and form a ball of cells, as they travel towards the uterus. In the uterus the ball of cells (called an **embryo**) sinks into the soft lining. This is called **implantation**. The woman is now **pregnant** and the menstrual cycle stops until after the baby is born.

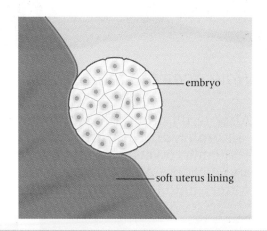

Twins

Sometimes, a woman might release two eggs at ovulation. If both are fertilised, twins are produced. These twins will not be identical. Sometimes, though, when the zygote divides in two, the two new cells get separated. Both of these cells now grow into an embryo and produce identical twins. Identical twins will either be two girls or two boys.

These twins are identical

These twins are non-identical

 Very occasionally, when the zygote divides in two, the two new cells start to separate (as if they were going to produce identical twins) but do not separate fully. In this case the twins will be joined together, often at the hip. Joined twins like this are often called Siamese twins.

4 Where does fertilisation occur?

5 Only one sperm cell joins with the egg cell. What do you think happens to all the others?

6 What is a fertilised egg cell called?

7 What is implantation?

8 How might a woman know she is pregnant?

9 a) How are non-identical twins produced?
  b) How are identical twins produced?

You should know...

- In sexual intercourse, the penis is inserted into the vagina.
- Fertilisation takes place when the nucleus of the sperm joins with the nucleus in the egg cell.
- This takes place in a fallopian tube and produces a zygote.
- The zygote divides into a ball of cells, called the embryo, which implants into the uterus lining.

How does the fetus develop during pregnancy?

After fertilisation, the zygote divides to form a ball of cells (an **embryo**). This **implants** into the soft lining of the uterus. The embryo gets food and oxygen from the blood in the soft uterus lining, to help it grow and develop. As it grows it becomes surrounded by a bag (the **amnion**) filled with a watery liquid (the **amniotic fluid**). The amniotic fluid protects the embryo as it grows.

> **?** **1** What protects the developing embryo?

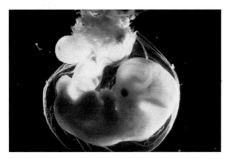 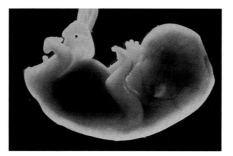 

*At five weeks the **embryo** is about 5 mm long. It has a small heart to pump blood*

*After about ten weeks it has a full set of organs. It is about 4 cm long and is now called a **fetus***

After about fifteen weeks the fetus is 16 cm long. The mother can now feel its movements inside her

The heart of the **fetus** (pronounced 'fee-tus') pumps blood around its body and the **placenta**. The placenta is shaped like a plate and is attached to the uterus lining. At the placenta, the fetus' blood gets food and oxygen from the mother's blood. Waste materials (like carbon dioxide) are given to the mother's blood. The **umbilical cord** carries blood between the fetus and the placenta.

> **?** **2** After how many weeks can the mother feel the baby move?
>
> **3** What is the job of:
> a) the placenta
> b) the umbilical cord?

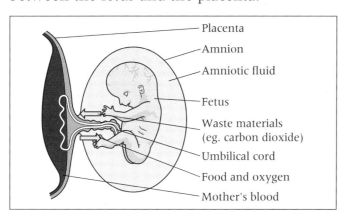

- Placenta
- Amnion
- Amniotic fluid
- Fetus
- Waste materials (eg. carbon dioxide)
- Umbilical cord
- Food and oxygen
- Mother's blood

> **?** **4** Why does the fetus' blood not mix with the mother's?
>
> **5** a) What does the fetus take from the mother's blood?
> b) What does the fetus give to the mother's blood?
>
> **6** The lungs do not work in a fetus. Why do you think this is?

The mother's blood does not mix with the fetus' blood. This is because the mother's blood is pumped around her body under a lot of pressure, which would damage the delicate fetus.

You should know...

● **How the developing fetus is protected and cared for in the uterus.**

How can a mother care for the developing fetus?

During pregnancy, many changes happen in a woman's body. Her heart will beat faster, she will become heavier and she will need more food for energy each day. It is important that the mother has a healthy diet during pregnancy. She must provide the fetus with food and vitamins.

 1 What changes will occur in a woman during pregnancy?

It is also important that the mother takes exercise to keep her muscles strong. She will need strong muscles during the birth.

 2 Why is exercise important during pregnancy?

There are some things that a woman should avoid during pregnancy. Alcohol, drugs and dangerous chemicals from cigarette smoke will all go through the placenta and into the fetus, where they can cause damage.

Too much alcohol will damage a fetus' brain (it can even cause severe brain damage). Illegal drugs, like heroin, also cause brain damage in the fetus.

Doctors are very careful about which medicines they give to pregnant women.

The blood of women who smoke carries less oxygen than it should, which means that the fetus may not get enough oxygen. A baby that has not received enough oxygen is likely to be born small and early (a **premature baby**).

*At an **ante-natal class**, mothers can do special exercises to strengthen their muscles*

 Sadly, sometimes drugs given to women to help them in pregnancy damage the fetus. In the 1950s a drug called thalidomide was taken by many pregnant women. It caused many babies to be born with very short arms and legs.

 3 a) What is a premature baby?
   b) Give one reason why this happens.

4 Which things should a mother avoid during pregnancy? Explain your answer.

You should know...
● **During pregnancy a woman must eat a good diet and avoid harmful things like smoking.**

What happens during and just after birth?

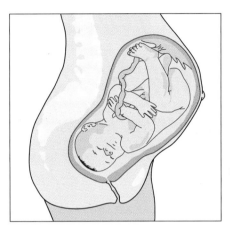

Pregnancy lasts about 9 months (40 weeks). When the baby is due to be born the uterus starts to push or **contract**. This is the start of **labour**. Labour ends when the baby is born. The contractions are gentle at first but become more powerful as labour moves on. The cervix then starts to get wider to allow the baby through. At some stage, the amnion breaks and the amniotic fluid rushes out of the vagina.

1 What are contractions?

2 Explain what happens to the cervix during labour.

Once the cervix is about 10 cm wide, the strong contractions of the uterus push the baby through it. Usually the head comes out first and the baby starts to breathe almost immediately. The umbilical cord is then tied and cut. The scar left by the umbilical cord becomes the **navel** or 'belly button'.

About half an hour after the birth, the placenta breaks away from the uterus and passes out through the vagina. This is called the **afterbirth**.

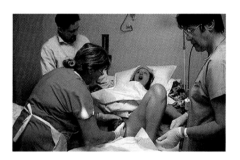

3 Why do people have navels?

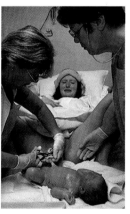

In the first few months, the baby needs to be fed on milk. The breasts contain **mammary glands** that produce milk. After a few months the baby can start to eat semi-solid food.

4 Copy and complete these sentences:

Pregnancy lasts for _____ months. When the baby is ready to be born, the uterus starts to _____ . The baby is normally born _____ first. After being born the _____ is cut. This leaves a scar called the _____ .

5 Explain what is meant by the 'afterbirth'.

6 How does a young baby get its food? Explain in as much detail as you can.

You should know...

● **Pregnancy lasts for 9 months.**

● **Contractions in the uterus push the baby out through the cervix and vagina.**

Fertility treatment

What do people do if they can't have a baby naturally?

Most parents choose to start a family when the time is right for them. However, for some couples it is difficult to start a family. This is often due to a problem with the man's or woman's reproductive organs. Both the man and the woman may go to a hospital to have tests to find out what is wrong.

 1 Why do you think people like to choose when to start a family?

Damaged or narrow fallopian tubes may stop sperm getting to the egg cells. In some cases, doctors can operate on the tubes to make them wider. If this does not work, the woman may be given a sex hormone to make her produce many egg cells all at once. These can be collected and added to the man's sperm cells in a special dish. The fertilised cells are then placed into the uterus lining, where they grow and develop.

Some men produce very few sperm cells (they have a low **sperm count**). In this case, a single sperm cell is taken and injected into an egg using a very fine needle. Again, the fertilised egg is placed into the uterus lining.

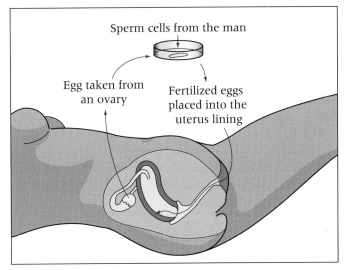

Sperm cells from the man

Egg taken from an ovary

Fertilized eggs placed into the uterus lining

These methods of helping couples have a baby are called **IVF** ('in vitro fertilisation'). Babies born to couples who have used IVF are often called **test-tube babies**.

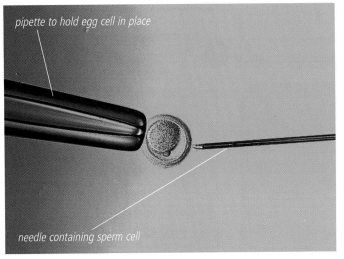

pipette to hold egg cell in place

needle containing sperm cell

 2 a) What does IVF stand for?
  b) Why do some couples use IVF to help them have a baby?
  c) Try to find out what the words 'in vitro' mean. (*Hint*: it's Latin.)

 The world's first 'test-tube baby', Louise Brown, was born in Oldham in 1978.

How do we know if something has dissolved?

When salt is stirred into water, the salt **dissolves**. The salt grains seem to disappear. They completely split up and mix in with the water. We say that salt is **soluble** in water.

1 Write down the name of:
  a) another solid that dissolves in water
  b) a solid that does not dissolve in water.

Beaker 1   Beaker 2   Beaker 3

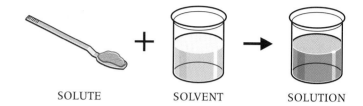

SOLUTE   SOLVENT   SOLUTION

A solid dissolved in a liquid makes a **solution**. Beaker 1 contains a solution. There is a solid dissolved in the water. A solution is always **transparent** (see-through) even if it has a colour. In a solution, the liquid is called the **solvent**, and the solid is called the **solute**.

Beaker 2 contains milk. Milk contains water with some fat. The fat has not completely dissolved in the water. We know this because the liquid is cloudy.

Beaker 3 contains flour and water. Stirring it makes the liquid go cloudy but soon all the grains of flour sink to the bottom. Flour does not dissolve in water. It is **insoluble**.

2 In a cup of instant coffee:
  a) What is the solvent?
  b) What is the solute?

3 How can you tell if:
  a) a solid has dissolved
  b) a solid has not dissolved?

You can only taste substances that dissolve in the moisture on your tongue. You cannot taste insoluble substances.

You have five different chemicals. How would you find out if they dissolve or not?
● What would you look for?

4 Write down what these words mean:
  a) dissolve   b) solvent
  c) soluble   d) solute.

5 In the beakers on this page, which ones contain a liquid that is:
  a) transparent
  b) coloured
  c) colourless?

You should know...

● **Some solids dissolve in water to make a solution. These solids are soluble.**

● **A solution contains a solute (solid) and a solvent (liquid).**

● **A solution is always transparent.**

● **Solids that do not dissolve are insoluble.**

What is the difference between melting and dissolving?

If margarine is heated it will **melt** and turn into a liquid. When it cools down, the margarine will turn back into a solid. **Melting** involves one substance and always needs heat.

Dissolving always needs at least two substances. Usually one of these is a solid and one is a liquid. Some gases also dissolve in liquids – for example, the 'fizz' in fizzy drinks is due to dissolved carbon dioxide.

---

1 Copy and complete these sentences:

When a solid dissolves in a liquid, it makes a _____ .

The solid is called the _____ and the liquid is called the _____ .

2 Write down these changes, and say whether each one is melting or dissolving:
a) ice turning to water
b) stirring sugar into tea
c) chocolate going runny

3 a) In this drink, what is the solvent?
b) Write down the names of three solutes in the drink.

Essential Ingredients:
Carbonated Water, Colour E150d, Phosphoric Acid., Sweeteners (Aspartame, Acesulfame-K), Acidity Regulator (Sodium Citrate), Preservative (Sodium Benzoate), Flavourings. Caffine Contains a source of Phenylalanine.

When you make a solution, the solute does not go away. The solute you use all stays in the solution. The total mass of a solution is always equal to the mass of solvent added to the mass of solute.

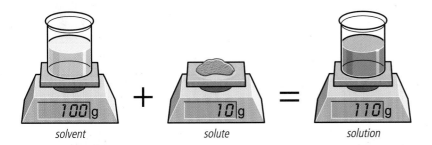

| solvent | | solute | | solution |

100 g + 10 g = 110 g

You should know...

- Solids can melt when they are heated. They change back when they cool down.

- Dissolving occurs when a soluble solid mixes in with a liquid.

- Mass of solvent + mass of solute = mass of solution.

4 On a copy of this table, fill in the missing masses:

Mass of solvent	Mass of solute	Mass of solution
50 g	2 g	
90 g		110 g
	45 g	100 g

How much solute can we dissolve?

There are very few things which are totally insoluble, although the amount that dissolves might be very small.

 1 Write down the names of:
  a) two substances that dissolve easily
  b) two substances that do not dissolve very well.

Even soluble solids like sugar cannot keep on dissolving forever. For example, you wouldn't expect a whole bag of sugar to dissolve in a glass of water. To find out how much of the sugar dissolves, you could add it, a little at a time, and stir. Eventually you would find that no more sugar will dissolve.

 2 How could you tell that the sugar had stopped dissolving?

When no more sugar will dissolve, there will be some crystals left at the bottom of the glass. The solution is now **saturated**. It contains as much dissolved solid as it possibly can. If you add more sugar, it will sink to the bottom and stay undissolved.

 3 Are these statements true or false? If you think one is false, explain why:
  a) Almost all solids will dissolve a little in water.
  b) If you add more solid to a saturated solution it will dissolve.
  c) If you add more solid to an unsaturated solution it will dissolve.

How could you find out if more salt or more sugar dissolved in water?
● What would you measure?
● How would you make it a fair test?

 Even sand dissolves! Sand is made of a chemical called silica. 0.1 g of silica will dissolve in a litre of water. Sponges can extract the silica from sea water and use it to help build their bodies.

In the first beaker 34 g of solid have dissolved in 100 cm^3 of water to make a saturated solution. The second beaker has twice as much water, so twice the mass of solid will dissolve (68 g).

The temperature also affects the amount of a solid that dissolves. More solid dissolves when the water is hotter.

4 Write down two factors that affect the amount of solid needed to make a saturated solution.

5 Milk of Magnesia is an indigestion remedy which contains magnesium oxide. How can you tell from the picture that not all of the magnesium oxide has dissolved?
(You might need to look back at page 58).

6 Are these statements true or false?
   If you think one is false, explain why:
   a) If you add more liquid to a saturated solution more of the solid will dissolve.
   b) If you stir a saturated solution more of the solid will dissolve.
   c) If you heat a saturated solution more of the solid will dissolve.
   d) If you pour the water into a wide, shallow dish, more solid will dissolve

You should know…

● **When no more solute can be dissolved in a solution, it is said to be saturated.**

● **The amount of solute that dissolves depends on the volume of solvent (e.g. water) and its temperature.**

How can we make things dissolve faster?

Some people add sugar to their tea and coffee to make it taste sweet. They are not interested in the total amount of sugar that could possibly dissolve in the water. The most important thing is to get the sugar to dissolve quickly.

 1 If you want the sugar in your tea to dissolve quickly, what do you do?

Three important factors (or **variables**) affect the time it takes for something to dissolve:
- the temperature of the water
- the size of the pieces
- whether you stir the water or not.

 How would you find out how each of these factors changes the time that sugar takes to dissolve?
- How would you make it a fair test?

Solids dissolve more quickly when the temperature is higher. The size of the pieces is also important. Sugar lumps take longer to dissolve than granules. This is because the water cannot get to the inside of the lump until the outer layers have dissolved. The granules are much smaller, so more sugar is in contact with the water.

 2 An experiment is carried out to investigate whether granules dissolve faster than lumps. Write down three factors that would need to be kept the same to make it a fair test.

Even granules won't dissolve easily if they are at the bottom of the cup, covered by another layer of sugar – the water cannot get to them. So, stirring will also help the sugar to dissolve. Stirring moves the granules around so that they mix well with the water.

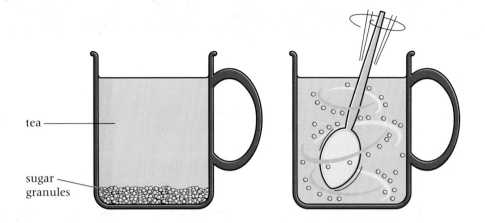

tea

sugar granules

3 In which of these two situations would the sugar dissolve faster? Explain your reasons in each case:
a) 1 lump of sugar in water at 20°C, or 1 lump of sugar in water at 50°C.
b) 5 g of sugar in a lump, or 5 g of sugar in granules, each in 100 cm^3 of water.
c) 10 g of sugar granules in 100 cm^3 of water with stirring, or without stirring.
d) 10 g of sugar in 100 cm^3 of water, or 10 g of sugar in 250 cm^3 of water.

If you open a warm bottle of fizzy drink, it will often 'froth up'. This is because gases are less soluble in warm water than in cold. As the drink warms up, the gas tries to bubble out of the solution. If the lid is screwed on tight, it cannot escape – until you take the top off!

4 The instructions on a bottle of lemonade say:
'Open with care. Point away from the face and cover the top. Keep cool, out of direct sunlight. Best served chilled.'
Explain why it says this on the bottle.

Oxygen from the air dissolves in water. Fish use gills to take this oxygen out of the water again. Many fish die in very hot weather because there is less oxygen dissolved in the water.

You should know...
● You can make something dissolve more quickly by stirring it, by crushing it into smaller pieces, or by heating the water.

How can we remove ink or paint marks?

Ink marks can be a nuisance. A damp cloth will get rid of the marks if the ink is soluble in water. Even 'permanent' pens are not totally permanent. The word normally means the ink will not dissolve in water.

Ink marks that cannot be removed using water can often be removed using a different solvent such as methylated spirit or propanone (nail varnish remover).

 P How could you find out which was the best solvent for cleaning up ink marks?
- What would you do to make sure this was a fair test?
- How will you judge if each solvent has worked?

 'Dry cleaning' was invented by Jean-Baptiste Jolly in 1825. He got the idea by finding that a patch of a tablecloth on which paraffin had been spilt was cleaner than the rest of the cloth.

Some paints can be washed off with water, but gloss paint cannot. A solvent called white spirit is used to remove gloss paint. Gloss paint is soluble in white spirit but not in water.

Oil cannot be removed from clothes using water but it can be removed using a solvent called paraffin.

Washing in water will damage some fabrics – they need to be 'dry cleaned'. This means that no water is used. A different solvent (perchloroethylene) is used to remove the dirt without ruining the clothes.

 1 a) Explain what a solvent is.
   b) Name four different solvents.

2 Car mechanics often get engine oil on their clothes. Explain why water is not very good for removing the stains. What might you use to get the stain off?

3 Explain why:
   a) 'dry cleaning' is not really dry
   b) the term 'dry cleaning' is used.

You should know...
- Water is the most common solvent.
- Other liquids can also be used as solvents.
- Solutes which are insoluble in water may dissolve in other solvents.

What are the dangers of solvents?

Some solvents are dangerous, so you must know how to use them safely. Teachers check the **hazards** of the chemicals that you use, to make sure you are safe. You should also check the hazards of the chemicals and apparatus that you plan to use in investigations.

HARMFUL

TOXIC

> **!** *A group of substances called CFCs used to be used as solvents. These are now banned because they damage the ozone layer. Scientists have found other safer chemicals to use instead.*

Things containing dangerous solvents show a **hazard warning symbol**. Poisonous (**toxic**) solvents show the 'skull and crossbones' warning symbol. Dry cleaning liquids and some glues contain solvents that are harmful if you breathe in the fumes. If you use them:

- be very careful
- only use small amounts
- use in a well ventilated area.

Products containing dangerous solvents cannot be sold to people under the age of 16.

> **?** 1 Explain why:
>   a) Dry cleaning machines are fitted with good extractor fans.
>   b) Some dry cleaned clothes have a label saying: 'If you are driving home, leave a window open'.
>
> 2 Write down another word meaning 'poisonous'.
>
> 3 A 'dry white board marker pen' has a label that says that it is 'xylene free'. Xylene is a hazardous chemical.
>   a) What happens to the solvent in the ink when writing on the white board?
>   b) What is the advantage of this type of pen over a normal 'marker pen'?
>   c) Why do you think the label says 'xylene free'?

What is an indicator?

Many flowers and fruits have bright colours and many coloured dyes can be obtained from them.

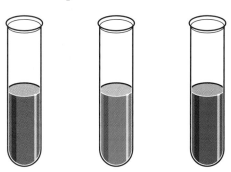

Some dyes can change colour when they mix with certain chemicals. A dye which can change colour is called an **indicator**. One example is **litmus**. This can be red or blue, or sometimes purple (blue and red together). You can also get litmus paper, which changes colour in the same way.

 How could you see if red cabbage worked as an indicator?
- What would you do to the leaves to get the colour out?
- How could you separate the coloured juice from the leaves?

One group of substances can turn litmus red. This group includes vinegar and fruit juices. These substances are similar in another way – they all have a sharp, sour taste. We call this group of substances **acids**.

Some acids, like hydrochloric acid, are too dangerous to taste. These stronger acids can be **corrosive**. This means that they can attack metals, stonework and skin.

Acid rain occurs when polluting gases are released into the air from car exhausts, power stations or factory chimneys. These gases dissolve in rain drops to form sulphuric acid and nitric acid.

Acids can be good for you too. For example, vitamin C is **ascorbic acid**. Some acids are used to give a tangy taste to fizzy drinks, sauces and ketchup.

 Your stomach contains strong hydrochloric acid. The wall of the stomach produces a special substance to stop the acid attacking the stomach wall. If you get stomach acid on your skin it will burn – this is why your throat gets very sore when you have been sick.

1 Name four acids.

2 What does the word 'corrosive' mean?

3 Give one example of acids being:
   a) useful
   b) harmful.

You should know...

- Litmus is an indicator which is red in acids.

- Vinegar and fruit juices are acids.

What is an alkali?

In ancient times, Arabic scientists took ashes from fires and mixed them with water. This liquid was boiled with animal fats to make the first soap. In Arabic, the ashes were called 'al kali'. We use the word **alkali** to describe a group of substances that feel soapy. However, many alkalis are too dangerous to feel.

In some ways, alkalis are the opposite of acids. They make indicators go a different colour. Alkalis turn litmus blue.

 How could you use this colour chart to find out if something is an acid or an alkali?
● What apparatus would you use?

| acid | neutral | alkali |

1 An indicator called methyl orange turns red in acid, and yellow in alkali:
  a) What colour would this indicator turn with grapefruit juice?
  b) What colour would it turn with oven cleaner?

Like acids, some alkalis are very corrosive. If you spill some acid or alkali on your skin, wash it off with plenty of water. Whenever you use acids or alkalis, you must wear eye protection because they can cause severe eye damage.

Many substances are neither acids nor alkalis. These are called **neutral**. Pure water, salt and sugar are all neutral. Neutral substances do not affect indicators at all.

Alkalis and acids cancel each other out to make neutral substances. For example, toothpastes contain a mild alkali to get rid of some of the acid in your mouth.

You should know...

● Litmus turns blue in alkalis.

● Alkalis can cancel out acids, making them neutral.

● Some alkalis are dangerous.

2 What is a 'neutral' substance?

3 State whether these substances are acid, alkali or neutral:
  a) vinegar   b) water   c) salt
  d) lemon juice e) toothpaste f) sugar
  g) soap.

How can we make a better indicator?

Indicators can show us whether something is an acid, an alkali or neutral. However, simple indicators cannot tell us whether an acid or alkali is **strong** or **weak**.

To find this out, we use a mixture of indicators to give a range of different colours. This mixture is called **universal indicator** and it will go a certain colour depending on the strength of the acid or alkali.

Universal indicator comes as a liquid or as test papers. It gives the same range of colours as a rainbow: red, orange, yellow, green, blue and purple. We can use it to place substances on a numbered scale which runs from 1 to 14. This is known as the **pH scale**.

 1 a) What is universal indicator?
b) What is it used for?

 In 1909 Søren Peter Sørensen, a Danish chemist, designed the pH scale in an effort to control the quality of beer manufacture.

strong acid			weak acid			neutral	weak alkali			strong alkali			
1	2	3	4	5	6	7	8	9	10	11	12	13	14

stomach acid — vinegar — skin — pure water — indigestion powders — washing powder — oven cleaner

lemon juice — fizzy drinks — milk — blood — toothpaste

pHs of different substances

 2 a) What pH number would a substance have if it turned universal indicator red?
b) Would it be an acid or an alkali?
c) Would it be strong or weak?

Many skin products now advertise their pH value. Your skin is naturally slightly acid: it has a pH of about 5.5. Most soaps are alkaline, with a pH of about 9 or 10. Some people find that using soap can dry out their skin and so some manufacturers have now developed alternatives that match the pH of skin.

Most shampoos and shower gels are slightly acidic, though they may not all match the pH of skin precisely.

3 What colour would a soap with a pH of 5.5 turn universal indicator?

P How could you find out the pH of different skin products?
- What apparatus will you need?

The hydrochloric acid in your stomach has a pH of 1 or 2. This acid helps to break down your food. If you produce too much acid, you may suffer from indigestion, or heartburn.

Remedies like Milk of Magnesia are called **antacids**. They contain alkalis to cancel out some of the acid. The alkalis are weak, so that they do not make your stomach too alkaline. Indigestion remedies are usually about pH 9.

4 a) What is 'heartburn'?
   b) What can be done to relieve the symptoms?
   c) Why does this work?

5 What is the pH of:
   a) stomach acid   b) pure water
   c) skin   d) Milk of Magnesia
   e) soap?

6 Copy and complete the following table:

Name of chemical	Colour of universal indicator	Acid, alkali or neutral	pH
Hydrochloric acid		Strong acid	
			7
Milk of Magnesia			
Sodium hydroxide	Purple		
Carbon dioxide solution		Weak acid	

7 A student spilt some acid on the bench, and asked the teacher for some strong alkali to help get rid of it. Explain why this is not a good idea.

You should know...

- The strengths of acids and alkalis can be measured on the pH scale.

- pH numbers 1 to 6 are acids, 7 is neutral, and 8 to 14 are alkalis.

- You can find out the pH number using universal indicator.

How can we make use of everyday mixtures?

If lots of different things are jumbled up together, we have a **mixture**.

This might just look like a pile of rubbish but it is possible to make use of most of it again! First it needs to be sorted into different materials.

1 What is a mixture?

2 Make a list of the different materials in the photograph that could be re-used.

When a car is scrapped it can be taken apart so that the different materials are separated. Each of the materials can then be re-used or **recycled**.

A pile of rubbish from the dustbin can be sorted out in the same way. A lot of packaging now has symbols on it to help us.

 Every part of a BMW car has a code printed on it to make it easier to sort out the different materials for recycling.

If rubbish is sorted into different piles when it is thrown away, it is much easier to recycle the materials. In some parts of the country, houses are provided with different boxes for different types of rubbish and these are then collected separately.

Bottle, newspaper and can banks are found in many towns to encourage us to recycle our waste materials.

3 How do bottle and can banks make it easier to recycle our rubbish?

Rubbish isn't the only mixture we come across every day. Most materials are mixtures made up from different things mixed together.

The air we breathe is actually a mixture of different gases which can be separated from each other. **Oxygen** can be separated from air and used in life support machines in hospitals.

Rocks are mixtures. They are made from different **minerals** which have been squashed together. A mineral is a chemical, such as sand or diamond, which is useful or beautiful to look at. We must separate the mineral we want from the other bits of rock before we can use it.

Sea water is another mixture. It is mostly water, but it has many different chemicals in it, including salt. The salt is useful and can be separated from the sea water. The sea water also carries rubbish, seaweed and sand with it. These can all be separated from the water.

 4 a) Write down three mixtures shown in the picture of the beach.
   b) Write down one useful thing we can get from each mixture.

 5 Recycling is a good way of looking after the Earth's resources. Design a poster to encourage students in your school to recycle more of their waste. Make sure you explain how to recycle the waste and why it is important to recycle our materials.

P Hammy, the unhappy hamster

Hammy the hamster is very fussy. He plays in sand during the day and sleeps in sawdust at night. If he mixes the sand and sawdust up whilst he is playing he cannot get to sleep in the mixture! Help Hammy by designing a way to separate the sand and sawdust so that he can get to sleep again.

You should know...

- A mixture is different materials mixed together.
- Examples of some useful things obtained from some everyday mixtures.

Fit to drink

How do we get clean water?

The water you use today has been used before. In fact it is possible that some of the water that you drink today will have been drunk before – possibly by someone famous!

Before we can drink a glass of water it must be cleaned. We would not dream of drinking a glass of water if it had just come out of the river in this picture.

1 Write a list of the rubbish shown in the photograph of the polluted river.

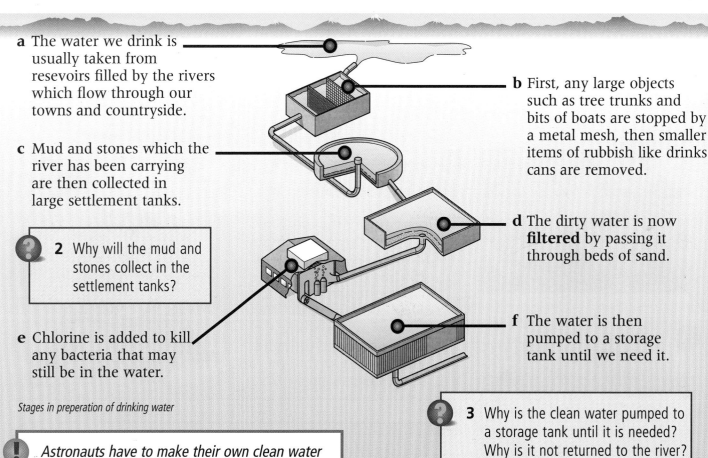

a The water we drink is usually taken from resevoirs filled by the rivers which flow through our towns and countryside.

b First, any large objects such as tree trunks and bits of boats are stopped by a metal mesh, then smaller items of rubbish like drinks cans are removed.

c Mud and stones which the river has been carrying are then collected in large settlement tanks.

d The dirty water is now **filtered** by passing it through beds of sand.

2 Why will the mud and stones collect in the settlement tanks?

e Chlorine is added to kill any bacteria that may still be in the water.

f The water is then pumped to a storage tank until we need it.

Stages in preperation of drinking water

3 Why is the clean water pumped to a storage tank until it is needed? Why is it not returned to the river?

! *Astronauts have to make their own clean water in space, using their urine.*

Filtering

The first three stages in cleaning the water involve **filtering**. Filtering is a way to separate the water from substances which do not dissolve in it.

A tea bag is another example of filtering in action. This filters the tea and keeps the tea leaves inside the bag so they can be thrown away and not drunk.

Filtering will not separate substances which are dissolved in the water, as these substances will be small enough to pass through the paper filter or through the gaps between the grains of the sand filter.

 4 Write a sentence to explain what a filter does.

> ! Around the world 25,000 people die every day from diseases caused by dirty drinking water.

 You can't always get clean water from a tap. Survival experts have to make their own clean water.

Design a piece of equipment which you could use to make clean (colourless) water in the countryside.

This equipment might be useful

 5 Write down the four stages in cleaning water and say what is removed from the water during each one.

6 Some water supplies come from natural springs underground. The water from these springs is usually very clean. Think about where the water will have come from and explain why it is so clean.

You should know...

- Filtering can be used to separate solid particles which do not dissolve from the liquid that is holding them.

- Filtering can not be used to separate particles which dissolve in the liquid.

Why doesn't all water taste the same?

Different parts of the United Kingdom are known for their drinks. For example, whisky is made in some parts of Scotland and beer is brewed in the Midlands. Why isn't whisky made in Birmingham? It may seem a silly question, but the answer lies in the water! The taste of these drinks is changed if different water is used to make them.

Even bottles of water from different parts of the country taste different. Labels on the bottles of water tell us what the bottle contains – it isn't just water. Water disolves chemicals from rocks as it flows over them and these dissolved chemicals give the water its taste. Different rocks contain different chemicals and so the taste of the water depends on where it comes from.

Different substances found in mineral waters

	Volvic (mg/litre)	Highland Spring (mg/litre)	Malvern (mg/litre)
Calcium	10	35	35
Magnesium	6	9	15
Sodium	9	6	15
Potassium	6	1	1
Bicarbonate	65	136	123
Chloride	8	8	39
Sulphate	7	6	35
Nitrate	6	0	8

 1 Why do different samples of water have a different taste?

We can show that the water contains these chemicals by heating the water. The water will **evaporate** and leave behind the chemicals which were dissolved in it. If we evaporate different water samples, we will get different amounts of these chemicals.

 2 Which water contains the greatest mass of chemicals?

 Salts are important for a healthy diet. Roman soldiers used to receive common salt as part of their pay.

The chemicals which are left behind are called **salts**. Our bodies need salts to stay healthy. We can get lots of salt from sea water if we let the heat of the Sun evaporate the water for us. The main salt in seawater is **common salt**, often just called 'salt'.

Collecting salt made from the evaporation of sea water in Africa.

 3 How does the Sun help us to get salt?

In Cheshire, England, salt is found in thick layers underground. This salt can be mined leaving large caverns. The salt can also be removed by pumping water into the ground. This water dissolves the salt, making salt solution or **brine**. The brine is then pumped back to the surface and heated to evaporate the water.

 4 Write a sentence to explain how we can get the salt out of water.

5 Why do you think the sea tastes salty? Where has the salt come from? How did it get there?

6 Imagine that you work for a company which makes salt by evaporating sea water using the salt-bed method. Describe your job and give details of the difficulties of getting salt in this way.

 How could you get the salt from a beaker of sea water, using the apparatus in your laboratory.

You should know...

● Most water has small amounts of salt dissolved in it.

● If you evaporate the water the salt is left behind.

How can we make pure water?

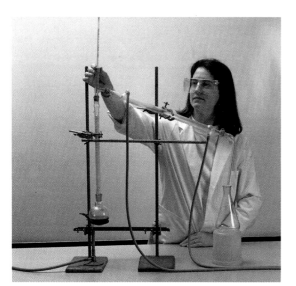

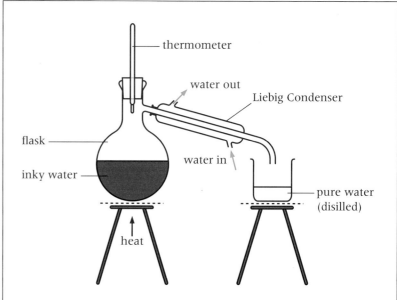

Pure water contains nothing but water. To get pure water, we must take the water out of the mixture, leaving everything else behind. We can do this by heating the mixture until the water boils. The picture shows the apparatus used to separate pure water from a mixture of ink and water.

When water is heated, it turns into a **gas** called **water vapour** or **steam**. The gas leaves the mixture of ink and water and rises up the tube. It is then collected and cooled to turn it back into a liquid. This is called **condensing**. To do this, a **condenser** is used. A condenser works by cooling down the glass tube, so that the steam becomes liquid water again. The liquid water is collected in the beaker.

This process of separating a liquid by evaporating it and then condensing it
is called **distillation**. The whole set of apparatus used is called a **still**.

Distillation can also be used to separate a mixture of liquids. For example, it is used to get alcohol from a mixture of water and alcohol during whisky production. The copper 'still' in the photograph is the apparatus which is used to do this. Although it is much bigger than laboratory apparatus, it works in the same way.

 1 How can we turn the water vapour back into liquid water?

 It is illegal to set up a distillery unless you have a licence and pay a fee to the government , called 'duty', for each litre of alcohol you produce.

 2 Why is the copper still much bigger than laboratory equipment?

Crude oil is found underground, beneath layers of rock. It is a mixture of different liquids which can be separated by a type of distillation called **fractional distillation**. The crude oil is heated in a **fractionating tower**. The different substances rise to different levels in the tower, depending on how easy they are to turn into gases. The ones with the lowest boiling points are the easiest to turn into gases and get to the top of the tower. All of the substances shown below can be obtained from one barrel of crude oil by distillation.

These materials all come from crude oil

3 Make a list of all the things in your room which are made from one of the materials obtained from crude oil.

4 Copy and complete these sentences:
Water is only _____ if it has nothing else dissolved in it.
We can get pure water using _____ . This process involves _____ the water to make _____ and then _____ the steam back to liquid.

5 Imagine that your best friend has missed this science lesson. Write a few sentences so that they will understand what distillation is and what it can be used for.

In 1872 Charles Wilson invented a cheap way of providing clean water in poor areas of the world. He devised a solar-powered water still.

You should know...

- **Distillation is evaporation followed by condensation.**
- **What mixtures distillation can be used to separate.**

How can we get pure water from sea water?

Pure water is needed for drinking. Some countries do not have enough pure water and have to make more from sea water. To do this, they must remove the salt from the water. This is known as **desalination**.

 1 What is desalination?

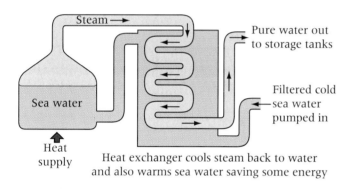

Steam →

Pure water out to storage tanks

Sea water

Filtered cold sea water pumped in

Heat supply

Heat exchanger cools steam back to water and also warms sea water saving some energy

The salt is usually removed from the sea water by distillation. The water is filtered to remove any insoluble particles and then boiled in a large tank. The steam rises, leaving the salt behind, and goes through a pipe into a **heat exchanger**.

The heat exchanger takes heat away from the steam and condenses it into pure water. The water can be bottled or piped to towns and cities.

 2 What does a heat exchanger do?

A desalination plant needs a lot of energy to boil large volumes of sea water. Sometimes the Sun's energy (solar power) is used to make the water boil. In other areas oil or gas is burnt to provide the heat, but this makes the water much more expensive to produce.

 Imagine you have been marooned on a desert island. How could you make drinking water from sea water using these items and sunlight?

 Cruise ships also use desalination plants. The QEII produces over 1 million litres of water each day from sea water.

 3 a) When the pure water is made from seawater, another substance is left behind. What is this other substance?

   b) How would you get rid of it?

What are the advantages and disadvantages of irrigation?

A supply of water is needed for growing crops in dry areas. The water is first collected in reservoirs created by damming rivers. The water then flows out of the reservoirs, through channels or pipes, to the dry fields. Watering the land by building channels or pipes is called **irrigation**.

Irrigation can also cause problems. Rivers carry fine soil particles called silt, which is a good natural fertiliser. When rivers flood, the silt settles on top of the soil in the surrounding fields. This makes the soil better for plant growing. A dammed river does not flood and so the silt never reaches the fields. The farmers then have to add artificial fertilisers to the land.

The silt collects in the reservoir, making it shallower so that it cannot hold as much water. The reservoir is said to 'silt up'.

 1 What is irrigation?

 Irrigation was first used by the ancient Egyptians who channelled water from the River Nile 7000 years ago.

Before

Floodplain made fertile by silt left when river floods

Floodplain   River

After

Old floodplain now above river level

Reservoir

Dam

Almost dry river bed with reduced water flow

As the water in the channels goes into the soil, the mineral salts dissolved in it also go into the soil. These mineral salts are needed by plants. If the water in the channels evaporates too fast, the mineral salts get left on the surface and the plants cannot get them.

2 a) What is silt?
   b) Why is silt important for a farmer's fields?

3 If the water evaporates from the channels to quickly, what happens to:
   a) the soil   b) the plants?

4 A desert is a very dry area of land. Describe how you would try to grow crops in a desert.

5 Why do you think large sums of money are spent on irrigation schemes like the ones on this page?

How can mixtures of dissolved solids be separated?

Orange dyes can be added to orange juice to make it look better. To find out if dye has been added, food scientists use **chromatography** to separate all the substances in the orange juice. The dye appears as a 'blob' that is not there in real 'pure orange juice'.

 1 Four orange drinks were tested. Which one has no added dye?

Chromatography works because different chemicals contain particles of different sizes. When dissolved in a liquid, the different sized particles travel through special paper at different speeds so that they separate out.

 2 Why do different substances travel different distances in chromatography?

After chromatography, the paper can be dried. The result is called a **chromatogram** and shows a pattern made up of all the colours in a mixture. Chromatography can be used to find out what colours are mixed together in different paints and inks. Each paint or ink mixture will make a different pattern.

 3 The ink shown in the photograph is a mixture of different colours:
  a) How many different colours are mixed together in the ink?
  b) Name these colours.

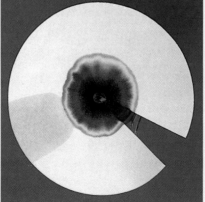

P. Police have found a letter written in brown felt tip at the scene of a crime. Five people were arrested because they have the same coloured pen. How could you find out which felt tip pen was used to write the letter?
- How will you get the ink off the original paper?
- How will you compare it with inks from the other five pens?
- How will you make it a fair test?

We can use chromatography to separate mixtures of many different chemicals. It is even used by the police in their investigations.

For example, samples of blood or skin are collected from the scene of a crime. Certain chemicals in these samples are compared with those from a suspect, using chromatography. If the samples match, it proves that the suspect was at the scene of the crime.

Chromatography is also used in drug-testing athletes. A sample of an athlete's blood is taken and tested to see whether any drugs have been taken before the race. It is important to check that no-one is taking drugs that could help them to win.

A scientist comparing 'DNA fingerprints'

The use of chromatography to identify criminals is called 'DNA fingerprinting'. It was invented in 1984 by Alec Jeffreys who is Professor of Genetics at the University of Leicester, England.

4 The picture below shows what happened when different orange squashes and food colourings were tested using chromatography.

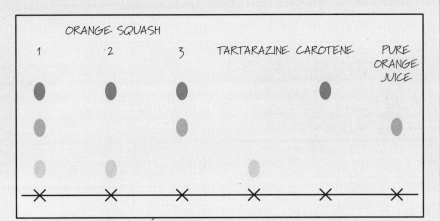

Use the picture to help you answer these questions.
Remember, if two marks are level with each other this means they are the same chemical:
a) Which food colourings are found in the three kinds of orange squash?
b) Tartrazine is thought to make some people over-active. Which orange squash would be safe to give to an over-active person? Why?
c) Why do you think Tartrazine is added to some orange squashes?

You should know...
● **What chromatography is, how it works and what it is used for.**

● **How to make a chromatogram.**

Why do different materials have different properties?

These items all look very different, and each is difficult to transport for a different reason. The items are either **solids**, **liquids** or **gases**.

 1 Look at the drawing carefully. Make a list of all the items you can see and then decide whether each item is a solid, a liquid or a gas.

We can tell solids, liquids and gases apart by looking at how each material behaves. Solids, liquids and gases have different **properties** which we can use to describe the differences between them.

All things are made of tiny pieces called **particles**. Solids, liquids and gases have different arrangements of particles. This gives them their special properties.

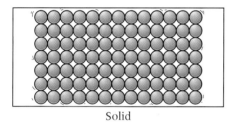
Solid

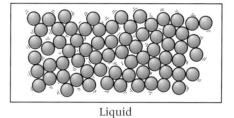
Liquid

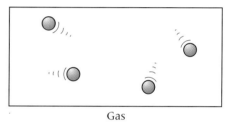
Gas

Solids have particles that are close together. The particles are fixed in place and cannot swap places with each other. That is why solids have a fixed shape

The particles in a liquid are still attached to one another but so weakly that they can move past each other. Liquids can change shape

In gases, the particles are not attached to each other and can move anywhere, by themselves. Gases can also change shape

We can change a solid into a liquid by heating it until it **melts**. The temperature when a solid becomes a liquid is called the **melting point** of the solid. The temperature when a liquid turns back into a solid is called the **freezing point**. The freezing point and melting point of a substance are always *the same* temperature.

 **2** What are all materials made from?

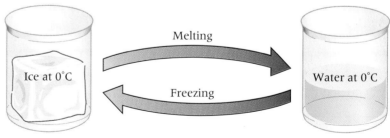

 3 a) What is the melting point of ice?
   b) What is the freezing point of water?

How would you find out if adding
salt to water changes its boiling point?
- Does it matter how much salt
  you use?
- How would you make sure your
  results are fair and reliable?

We can change a liquid into a gas by heating
it. The liquid **evaporates** into a gas. The
boiling point of a liquid is the temperature
when it is evaporating as fast as it can.

We can change a gas into a liquid by
cooling it down until the gas **condenses**
into a liquid.

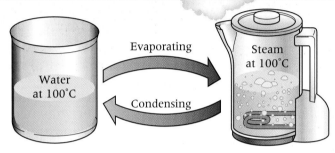

4 What decides whether a material is a solid,
   liquid or gas?

5 Iron and steel are solid materials. How could
   they be changed into liquids?

6 Design a poster to show how water can have
   three different forms. Show clearly how you
   would change water from one form into
   another.

You should know...

- Materials have different properties because they are made
  from particles which are arranged in different ways, making
  a solid, liquid or gas.

- A solid can be melted into a liquid by heating it.

- A liquid can be frozen into a solid by cooling it

- A liquid can be evaporated into gas by heating it.

- A gas can be condensed into a liquid by cooling it

- The meanings of the words evaporating, condensing, freezing
  and melting.

- For any substance, the freezing point and melting point are
  the same.

What is a solid?

This lorry is specially designed to carry a large bulky **solid** load. Once this turbine has been built, it has a shape that cannot be changed easily. The turbine cannot be easily squashed into a smaller space.

Solids also tend to stay in one place unless a force pushes or pulls them away. Once a solid object has been loaded onto a lorry, it stays there because a solid doesn't **flow**.

The turbine in the picture at the top of the page is very heavy for its size. We say that any object which is heavy for its volume is **dense**. Solids are often dense

 1 Write down the three properties of solids.

These solids have kept the same shape

Lead is a very dense solid. Wood is not a very dense solid

Calculating density

Density measures how much mass there is in 1 cm³ of something, The density of an object is worked out by finding its mass and dividing by its volume. You can use this formula.

$$\text{density} = \frac{\text{mass}}{\text{volume}}$$

To work out density you must make sure that you have measured the mass in grams and the volume in cm³.

 2 What is the density of a piece of wood that has a mass of 90 grams and a volume of 100 cm³?

Explaining the properties

P How could you find out if there is a connection between the density of an object and whether it floats or sinks?
- You will need to work out the densities of different objects
- You will also need to work out the density of water.

These properties of solids can all be explained if we have a closer look at how a solid is made up. Solids are made from tiny particles which are very close together and which cannot move around. Solids have a fixed shape because the particles are held tightly together by special forces called **bonds**.

These bonds are strong and they stop the particles moving apart. The bonds also stop the particles from flowing past each other. This stops the whole solid from flowing.

? **3** What holds the particles together in a solid?

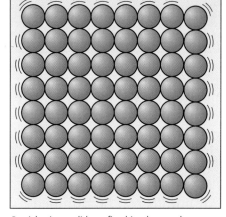

Particles in a solid are fixed in place and can only vibrate

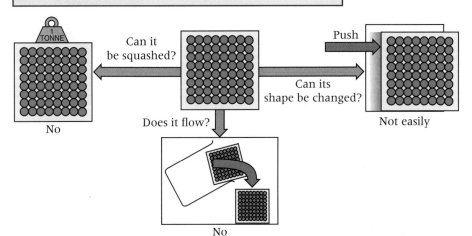

Things can only change their volume if the particles in them spread out or get closer together. In a solid, the particles are already very close together. This makes it very difficult for the volume of a solid to be made smaller.

? **4** Make a list of ten objects you can see around you which are solids. Explain how you know they are solids.

You should know...
- Solids are made up of particles that are very close together.
- Solids are difficult to squash, do not flow, have a fixed shape and volume, and have a high density.

C3c Liquid assets

Why do liquids flow?

It would be very difficult to transport water in the aquarium. The aquarium would be very heavy and the water would slosh about as it was moved. This shows us one of the important properties of **liquids** – they **flow**.

Some liquids flow more easily than others. For example, water flows more easily than treacle.

 1 How would you carry the fish home so that they didn't end up without any water?

If we want to carry a liquid, like water, we need a sealed container. If we want to carry water or milk around the country we use a tanker.

All liquids can be pumped into and out of tankers because the liquids can change shape. This means that a tanker can be filled and sent to the place where the liquid is needed, without spilling a drop.

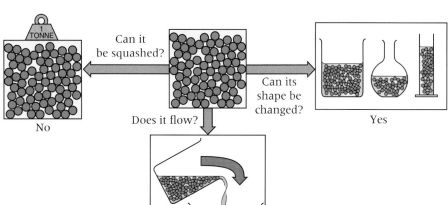

The volume of a liquid cannot be changed. Liquids cannot be squashed because the particles in a liquid are already close together.

Liquids are quite dense, but they are usually less dense than solids.

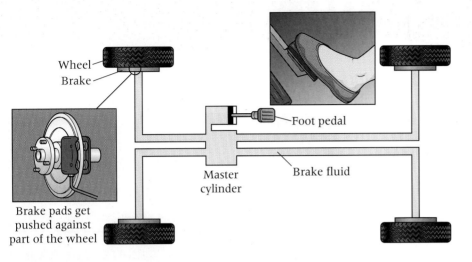

Wheel
Brake

Foot pedal

Master
cylinder

Brake fluid

Brake pads get
pushed against
part of the wheel

Liquids have a fixed volume and cannot be squashed. This makes them useful in car braking systems.

When the brake pedal is pressed, some brake fluid is pushed along the brake pipe. The brake pads are then pushed onto part of the wheel, making the car slow down. This would not work if the liquid could be squashed.

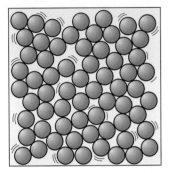

The particles in a liquid are close together but they can move past each other quite easily. The bonds in a liquid are weak enough to let the particles move about but strong enough to hold them together.

 2 Why is a liquid useful for making brakes work?

 3 What is a liquid? Write down the properties.

4 What are the differences between solids and liquids? Make a list of as many differences as you can. Make a table to show your answers:

Solids	Liquids
fixed shape	
	fixed volume

5 A friend of yours thinks that sand is a liquid! Is he right? (Think about the properties of liquids and solids, for example are there any differences between a single grain of sand and a lorry load of sand.)

P

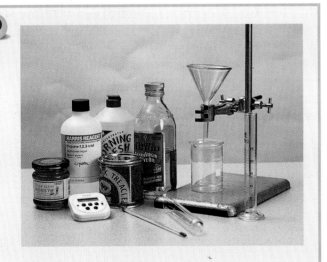

Different liquids have different densities. This means that a volume of one liquid might have a bigger mass than the same volume of another liquid.

• How would you find out if there is a connection between the density of a liquid and how easily it flows?
• What happens if the liquid is warmed?

You should know...

● Liquids are made up of particles that are fairly close together.

● Liquids cannot be squashed, flow quite easily, and have a fixed volume but no fixed shape.

● Although they are dense, liquids have a lower density than solids.

How are gases different from solids and liquids?

This diver has to carry all the air that she will need to breathe during her dive. The small cylinder on her back contains enough air to let her stay under the water for about an hour.

In one day, a person normally breathes the volume of air contained in a small room. We can only get all this air into a small cylinder if we squash it.

Air is a mixture of gases, and all gases can be squashed.

> **?** **1** How can a large amount of air be put into a small cylinder?

> **!** *A resting adult breathes in about 250 litres of air every hour.*

When we squash a gas, we make its volume smaller. Gases do not have a fixed volume – they fill the whole of the space they are in. When we put the gas into the cylinder, we change its shape and its volume.

Large amounts of gas can be transported by squashing it into a tank.

The particles in a gas are a long way apart. When we squash a gas, the particles are moved closer together – the more the gas is squashed, the closer together the particles will get.

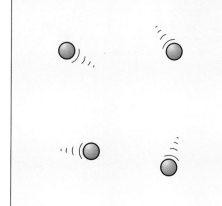

Particles in a gas are far apart and move quickly in any direction

> **?** **2** What happens to the particles if air is squashed into a smaller space?

Gases are not very dense. You can see that they are less dense than liquids if you take a bottle of fizzy drink and open it. Bubbles of gas float to the surface of the liquid. Gases are less dense than solids and liquids because there are fewer particles in a certain volume.

Particles in a gas are very far apart and moving very quickly in all directions. The particles are able to move wherever they like because there are no bonds between them. Therefore, a gas does not have a fixed volume or shape.

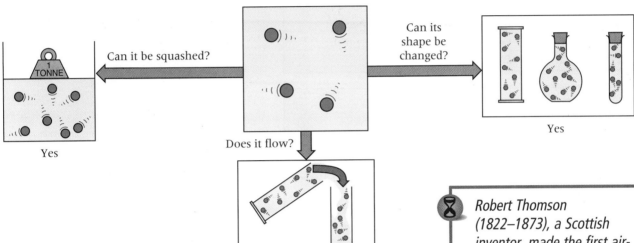

 How could you find out what effect heating or cooling an open bottle of fizzy drink has on the number of bubbles of gas it contains?

Robert Thomson (1822–1873), a Scottish inventor, made the first air-filled tyre in 1845. Air is a gas and so it can be squashed. This meant that the tyres were squashed when going over bumps. This made the ride more comfortable than the wooden wheels with iron rims that were used at the

3 Why are gas particles able to spread out to fill any space?

4 Make a list of all the properties of gases.

5 Why does air make a good material to put inside the tyres of a car or bicycle?

6 Why is it dangerous to drive a car which has air in the brake system?

7 Explain why a football which is full of air bounces when it hits the ground, but a football which is flat and needs pumping up doesn't bounce.

You should know...

● Gases are made up of particles that are well spread out.

● Gases are easy to squash, flow easily, have no fixed volume and no fixed shape.

● Gases have a lower density than liquids.

What is the difference between a solid, a liquid and a gas?

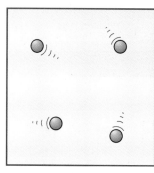

Gas
- Gases are made up of particles that are well spread out
- Gases are easy to squash, flow very easily, do not have a fixed volume and do not have a fixed shape
- Gases have a lower density than liquids

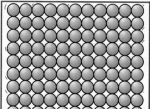

Solid
- Solids are made up of particles that are very close together
- Solids cannot be squashed, do not flow and have a fixed volume and shape
- Solids have a high density

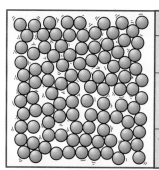

Liquid
- Liquids are made up of particles that are close together
- Liquids cannot be squashed, flow easily, have a fixed volume but no fixed shape
- Although they are dense, liquids have a lower density than solids

 1 Use the information above to describe the differences between:
   a) a solid and a liquid
   b) a solid and a gas
   c) a gas and a liquid.

2 What do solids, liquids and gases have in common?

Do solids and liquids expand?

When a solid or a liquid is heated, the particles begin to move further apart, making the material bigger. This is called **expansion**. Although the material gets bigger, there are still the same number of particles inside it, but they are more spread out.

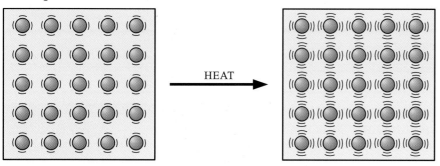

HEAT

The expansion of solids can cause a problem for designers. When a new road bridge is built, special expansion strips are added so that the bridge can expand in the summer heat without buckling and contract in the winter without leaving a gap.

Liquids also expand when they are heated. We can use this property of liquids to measure temperature changes. A thermometer is filled with a liquid which expands when it gets warmer and contracts when it gets colder.

Most liquids contract when they get colder. Water is different and expands when it cools below 4°C. This is why glass bottles which are full of water should never be put into a freezer.

1 What makes a material expand?

When a material is cooled, the particles move more slowly and get closer together. This is known as **contraction**.

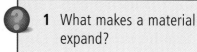

expansion joint

Concorde gets very hot when it flies. The equipment inside has special gaps built into it so that the equipment can expand 30 cm when the plane is in flight.

2 Explain how a thermometer works.

3 This railway line has been laid with a special expansion joint in it. Was this photograph taken on a hot or a cold day? What evidence in the photograph gives you the answer?

What is pressure?

Gases are made up of particles that are moving all over the place. As they move, the particles bump into each other and they also hit the sides of the container. The force of the particles hitting the side of the container causes **pressure**. If more particles hit the side of the container, there will be more pressure.

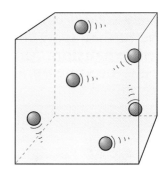

1 What causes pressure in the container of gas?

When we blow up a balloon, the rubber stretches and becomes much bigger than it was at the start. This is because the gas particles inside it are hitting the sides of the balloon and pushing it outwards.

If we squash a balloon full of air, it bursts. This is because the particles inside the balloon are still trying to move all over the place, but the space for them to move in has been made smaller. More particles bump into the sides of the balloon more often, creating more pressure. The rubber balloon is not strong enough to hold this pressure and so the balloon bursts, letting the air particles out.

Car tyres are filled with air to help the car move more smoothly. The gas particles in the air are moving about quickly, hitting the sides of the tyre. If too much air is put into the tyre, the pressure of the air hitting the inside of the tyre can make the tyre come off the rim of the wheel. This is known as a 'blow-out' and can cause a serious road accident.

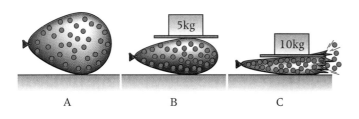

A   B   C

Wheel rim

Tyre being forced from wheel-rim

Tyre tread

2 Draw a poster for a tyre company to help them to explain why you must put the correct amount of air in your tyre.

Heating gases

What happens when we heat a gas?

The particles in a gas are moving all the time. If we heat the gas, the particles will move faster as they are given more energy. This will make them hit the sides of the container more often and so the pressure on the sides of the container will increase.

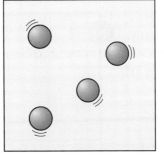 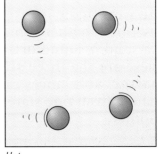

Cool   *Hot*

 1 Why will the pressure increase if a gas is heated?

A bigger pressure may make a container burst. As a car is driven along a road, the tyres get hot as they rub against the road. This heats up the gas particles inside the tyre, which increases the pressure in the tyre. If the car is driven too quickly, the gas particles may heat up so much that they push the tyre off the wheel rim, causing the tyre to 'blow out'.

 2 Why is a car tyre more likely to burst if the car is going very fast?

If the gas is heated inside a container which can get bigger, like a syringe, the volume of gas will increase because the gas particles are moving faster and spread out more. If the gas particles are more spread out, the mass of a fixed volume of gas will be less. This allows hot air balloons to fly upwards as the warm air inside the balloon is less dense than the colder air around the balloon.

P How would you find out how much the gas in a flask expands when it is heated gently using a water-bath?

How would you use your results to predict how much the gas in the flask would expand if it was heated to 100°C?

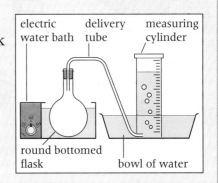

electric water bath · delivery tube · measuring cylinder · round bottomed flask · bowl of water

 3 How could you make the volume of a gas decrease without making the pressure increase?

What do we mean by the word 'state'?

The word 'state' is used to describe whether something is a solid, a liquid or a gas. These are the three **states of matter**. Substances can change from one state to another.

1 What are the three states of matter?

2 Sort these substances into solids, liquids and gases:

water	brick	air
petrol	steel	concrete
ice	carbon dioxide	oil

A Water turns to ice when it cools down

B Water in the kettle turns into steam

C Steam turns back into water when it hits a cold surface

D Ice cubes in a drink turn to water

E Sugar is stirred into a cup of tea

F Some of the liquid in the cup escapes into the air

3 In the picture, find three solids, three liquids and a gas.

4 Look at the boxes A to F. Which of these words describes what is happening in each box? Match each word to the correct letter:

freezing	boiling	dissolving
evaporating	condensing	melting

The volume of something is the amount of space it takes up:

- **Solids** have a fixed shape and volume.
- **Liquids** can flow, and can take up any shape. They also have a fixed volume.
- **Gases** can flow and will spread out to fill the whole container. Gases do not have a fixed volume. Gases are often invisible.

5 What does 'volume' mean?

6 a) Write down one way in which solids and liquids are different.

   b) Write down one way in which liquids and gases are similar.

The water in the kettle is **boiling**. It is changing very quickly from a liquid into a gas. This gas is called **steam** or **water vapour**. Changing from a liquid into a gas is called **evaporating**. When a liquid is boiling, it is evaporating as fast as it can.

7 Explain what the words 'evaporating' and 'boiling' mean.

8 How can you see when something is boiling?

Steam can change back into water again. This is called **condensation**. It happens when the steam from the kettle cools down and turns back into drops of water. The steam condenses and turns from a gas back into a liquid.

You can also see condensation when you breathe out on a cold day. Water vapour in your breath condenses in the air and turns into a liquid again.

This 'vapour trail' is made of water. Water vapour in the exhaust from the engines condenses to form water droplets

Many people say that you can see the steam coming from the kettle. In fact the steam is invisible. What you see is the drops of water that form when the steam cools down.

9 a) What is the state of steam?
   b) What state does it change into when it cools down?
   c) What is the name of this process?

10 Write down the different properties of solids, liquids and gases.

You should know...

- **The three states of matter and their properties.**

- **What boiling, evaporating and condensing mean.**

How can freezing make you hotter?

1 Write down two examples of liquids in the picture.

2 Describe the change of state (e.g. gas to liquid) that takes place when:
   a) the solid wax melts
   b) the wax goes up the wick and into the flame
   c) the wax runs down the side of the candle and freezes.

1 The top of the candle is hot. The heat from the flame is melting some of the solid wax so that it turns into a liquid

2 Some of this liquid wax then goes up the wick where it evaporates and turns into wax vapour (a gas). It is the wax vapour that burns in the flame.

3 Some of the liquid wax spills over the side of the candle. When it runs down the side, it cools down and turns back into a solid. This is an example of freezing.

You may think of freezing as a word which only describes cold things. This is because we are only used to thinking about water freezing. Water has to get very cold before it freezes and turns into ice. The freezing point of water is 0 °C.

P How could you find out what happens to the temperature of liquid wax if it is left to stand?
   • Make a prediction by sketching a graph of temperature against time.
   • What apparatus would you need.

With wax, the change from liquid to solid happens at a higher temperature. Liquid wax will freeze at about 50 °C. The melting point of solid wax and the freezing point of liquid wax are the same temperature.

! Carbon dioxide turns straight from a solid into a gas at −78°C without becoming a liquid. This is called **sublimation**. Solid carbon dioxide (known as 'dry ice') is used for special effects at concerts.

3 a) What is:
   i) the melting point of ice
   ii) the melting point of wax?

   b) Explain how you worked out your answers.

Changing from a solid to a liquid needs **heat energy**. When the liquid wax turns back into a solid, you get the heat energy back again. Dropping molten wax on your hand can be very painful. This is because the heat from the wax goes into your hand as it changes back into a solid.

 4 Why is it painful if you drop molten wax on your hand? Explain as fully as you can.

In the picture on the right, the ice cubes in the drinks are melting. For ice to melt, it needs heat. The heat comes from the rest of the drink. The drink gives some of its heat energy to the ice cube, so the drink gets colder. The ice cubes gain energy and turn from a solid into a liquid.

 5 Where does the heat come from to melt an ice cube in a glass of water?

If you hold an ice cube in your hand, you can feel the heat from your hand going into the ice cube. The heat of your body is being used to melt the ice.

It may seem strange, but we get this heat back again when the water freezes. To make ice, you put the water into a freezer. The freezer takes the heat away from the water and puts it into the room. Your fridge or freezer makes your kitchen warmer! The back of a fridge is warm, as the heat from inside is 'pumped out' into the room.

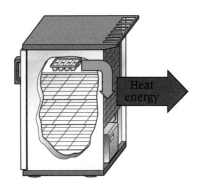

Heat energy

 6 A glass of water from the tap is usually at about 20 °C. Explain what would happen to the temperature of the water if:
a) you put an ice cube into it
b) you added more ice cubes
c) it was then left standing in the room for about an hour.

7 Design a poster to show all the changes of state, clearly showing what happens in each one and what each one is called.

You should know...
- **What melting and freezing mean.**
- **All changes of state involve heat energy moving from one place to another.**

How can freezing stop food and drinks going off?

Most foods have date labels on them. This tells you when it is safe to eat the food. If you eat the food after the 'use by' date you run a greater risk of getting an upset stomach.

SELL BY
JUNE 00
828AA 20:03

 1 Why do foods have a 'use by' date?

This fruit has got mould growing all over it, so it is clearly unfit to eat. Sometimes the problem is not so obvious – the food may look normal, but it could contain high levels of invisible bacteria, which can cause food poisoning. In extreme cases, people can die from food poisoning.

Keeping things cool is one way of keeping food fresh for longer. Bacteria feed and reproduce more slowly when it is cold. Food is safer to eat if it has been kept in the fridge.

Food keeps even longer in a freezer, with temperatures as low as −20°C. Frozen foods can be safely stored for several months. However, the bacteria are not killed off in a freezer – when the food is thawed, the bacteria start growing and reproducing again.

 2 How long could you store this product in a 'one star' frozen food compartment?

3 Which 'star rating' is the coldest type of freezer?

4 Explain why the storage times are different for the fridge and freezers.

5 Estimate the temperature inside a 'two star' freezer. Explain your reasoning.

6 Most frozen foods have a warning which says 'Do not refreeze this product after it has thawed out'. Why is it dangerous to freeze foods for a second time?

TO STORE	
Food Freezer ┐ † ✱ ✱ ✱ ✱	
'Star' Marked │ † ✱ ✱ ✱	3 Months
Frozen Food │ ✱ ✱	1 Month
Compartments ┘ ✱	1 Week
Ice Making Compartments	3 Days
Refrigerator	24 Hours

† Should be −18°C or colder

You should know...

- At room temperature, food goes off because bacteria grow and reproduce quite quickly. This can cause food poisoning.
- Bacteria grow and reproduce more slowly at low temperatures.

What happens when we try to freeze a mixture?

Pure water freezes at 0°C. On very cold nights, when the temperature is below zero, ponds freeze over but the sea does not. This is because salt water has a lower freezing point than pure water.

Rock salt is spread onto icy roads. The salt helps to melt the ice, even if the temperature is below zero. The sand and grit in the rock salt help to give a better grip.

 1 The sea rarely freezes in the United Kingdom. Why?

 P How would you find out how adding salt affects the freezing point of water?
- If you have a beaker of ice at 0°C, will the temperature keep going down as you add more salt? Make a prediction.
- How much salt would you add?
- How would you measure it out?

Adding sugar also affects the freezing point. Ice lollies need to be kept well below 0°C to stop them melting. The sugar and colourings make the freezing point less than zero.

 2 Why do ice lollies need to be kept well below the freezing point of water?

3 Gritting lorries spread rock salt onto roads to melt any ice that has formed. What does this tell you about the freezing point of salt water?

4 Ethanol (alcohol) has a freezing point of −117°C. If bottles of water and bottles of wine are put into a freezer at the same time, which one would freeze first? Explain your answer.

 In 1714 Gabriel Fahrenheit, a German scientist, built a thermometer. He needed a scale to put on the thermometer. He mixed ice with different types of salt. The salts lowered the freezing point, but some worked better than others. He decided that the temperature of the coldest mixture that he could make should be zero degrees on his scale. Zero degrees on the Fahrenheit scale is about −18°C.

What happens to water when we boil it?

To make a good cup of tea you need to make sure the water is boiling. To make it boil, you have to give the water more energy – that is, you need to heat it. The temperature of the water rises until it starts to boil. The boiling point of water is 100°C.

1 What is the boiling point of water?

2 What state does water turn into when it boils?

How would you find out how the temperature changes when you heat some water?
- What will be the temperature of the water when it boils?
- What will happen to the temperature of the water if you keep heating it after it has boiled? Make a prediction.

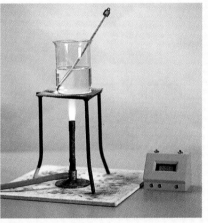

If you keep on heating the water, you might expect that the temperature would carry on rising. In fact, the water stays at the same temperature all the time it is boiling. The extra heat energy is being used to change the state of the water.

I always say you can't beat a good cuppa

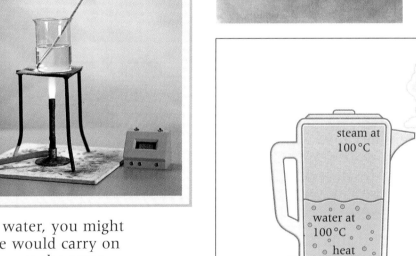

steam at 100°C

water at 100°C

heat

3 What happens to the temperature of the water once it is boiling?

4 What would happen to the mass of the water in a pan if you boiled it for 5 minutes? Explain your answer.

The liquid with the lowest boiling point is helium. Helium turns from a liquid into a gas at −269°C.

Water is made up of tiny invisible particles. They are always moving around. In liquid water, the particles are held together by special forces called **bonds**. When the water is heated, the particles move faster. As they move faster, they need more space to move around in and they knock each other out of the way. When they get very hot, they are moving so fast that the bonds can no longer hold them together. They break away from each other and form a gas which we call steam.

Steam contains more heat energy than water. When the steam condenses on the cold window, the heat from the steam goes into the glass. The steam gets cooler, and the window gets warmer.

 Warm water particles need more space to move around in than colder water particles. This means that there are fewer water particles in a litre of warm water than there are in a litre of cold water.

 5 Some machines for making cappuccino coffee or hot chocolate get the frothy effect by passing a jet of steam through the milky drink:
   a) What happens to the temperature of the steam when this happens?
   b) What happens to the temperature of the drink?
   c) Draw a diagram showing a jet of steam going into a drink. Add a red 'heat arrow' to show how the heat energy is transferred from the steam to the milk.

6 In terms of particles, explain what happens when water is heated until it boils.

7 What do you think happens to the particles in steam as it condenses?

You should know...
- **When it is boiling, the temperature of the liquid stays the same.**
- **What bonds are and what happens to them when water is heated.**

What happens if we keep on diluting?

When you make an orange drink, you have to mix the squash from the bottle with water. The squash is being **diluted**. The colouring and flavouring get spread out. We dilute things by adding more **solvent** (water in this case).

1 In the orange drink, what is the solvent and what is the solute?

2 a) What will happen to the colour of the drink when it is diluted with water?

   b) Explain why this happens.

If you pour some of the squash into a second glass and fill it up with water, it will be diluted even more. The second glass will contain less colour and flavour. You could pour some of this into a third glass and dilute it again. Eventually, you would get to a point where you could not see the colour any more.

P You are given a solution of a purple dye which contains 1 g of dye in every litre of solution. How could you find out the smallest amount of dye that could be seen with the naked eye?

• What apparatus would you need?

We can explain this observation using the idea of particles. We can imagine that the orange drink is made of orange particles mixed with water particles. The orange in the bottle contains a lot of orange particles and not many water particles. It is said to be **concentrated**.

When we dilute the drink, we take some of the mixture and add more water particles. Now there are less orange particles and more water particles, so the solution is less concentrated. Making something less concentrated is called **diluting**.

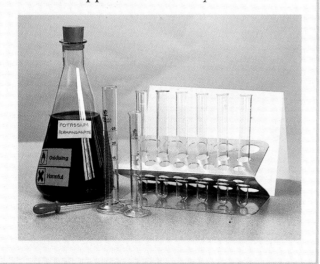

 There are about 30 000 000 000 000 000 000 000 000 particles in 1 litre of water.

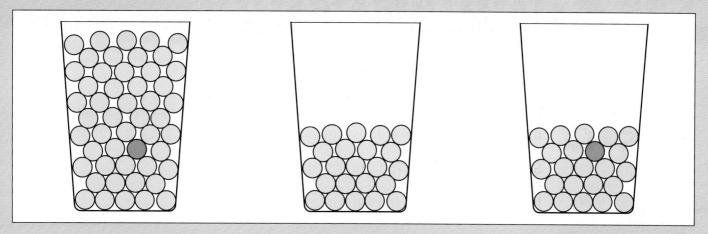

Imagine a really dilute solution with only one orange particle left in it. If you split this drink into two halves, only one half would get the orange particle. The other glass would now be pure water. Particles cannot be split in half. The particle has to go in one glass or the other.

The idea of particles is a **theory**. This means that scientists have used their imagination to think about how the drink might look if we could shrink ourselves down to a fraction of our normal size. The theory is used to explain the **observations**. A good theory can also be used to make **predictions** about what will happen in other experiments. These predictions can then be tested in new experiments.

3 Using the idea of particles, explain why the colour of orange squash gets less as you dilute it.

4 In your own words, explain the meanings of the words 'dilute' and 'concentrated'.

5 Read each of these sentences.
Decide if it is an observation, a theory or a prediction:
a) Blackcurrant juice is purple.
b) Blackcurrant juice contains tiny purple particles which make the juice coloured, as well as particles of water.
c) When you boil blackcurrant juice, the steam has no colour.
d) When blackcurrant juice boils, only the water particles have enough energy to escape. The purple particles are held back in the liquid.
e) Blackcurrant juice might freeze at a lower temperature than pure water.

You should know...

- **All drinks contain water. Most also contain colourings and flavours.**

- **All substances are made up of tiny particles.**

- **What dilute and concentrated mean.**

- **The differences between an observation, a theory and a prediction.**

How do the smells of cooking spread from the kitchen?

Imagine your favourite food being cooked in the kitchen. The smell can make you hungry. But how does the smell get to you?

Some 'smelly particles' are given off by the food. These particles then spread through the air. Some of them end up in your nose where you have special 'smell detectors'.

Even if the air is not moving, you will still notice the smell. This is because the gas particles are moving on their own. The way that a smell moves around a room like this is called **diffusion**. The 'smelly particles' are mixing with the air particles without anything moving them.

How could you measure the speed of diffusion through air?
- If the teacher puts some perfume into the dish, who would smell it first?
- How long would it take for the smell to reach the back of the room? Make a prediction.

Diffusion also happens in liquids. Tea is normally stirred to help the sugar dissolve quickly. Even if it is just left, the sugar will eventually dissolve on its own. The dissolved sugar particles will then diffuse through the tea. This diffusion takes a long time, as the particles in a liquid are moving more slowly than in a gas. There is also less space between the water particles for the sugar particles to move through. Diffusion in liquids may take several days.

1 What is diffusion?

2 Which is quicker, diffusion in liquids or gases? Explain why.

Diffusion also takes place when you make the tea. In boiling water, some of the tea from the tea bag starts to dissolve. The soluble tea particles dissolve and diffuse through the tea bag into the water. The tea leaves are too big to get through the gaps in the paper, so they stay inside the tea bag.

3 How can you tell that something from the tea leaves has dissolved in the water?

4 How do you know that tea leaves don't dissolve completely?

How could you find out how the speed of diffusion in liquids is affected by the temperature of the liquid?
- How would you observe or measure the speed of diffusion?
- How many different temperatures should you try?
- Which would be best to use: a tea bag or a spoonful of Bovril?

A glass of fizzy drink eventually goes flat. The gas bubbles out of the solution and mixes with the air. This is another example of diffusion. To stop the gas getting out you can put it in a bottle with a tight lid. Modern 'PET' (**p**oly**e**thylene **t**erephthalate) plastics can keep the gas in. Some other plastic bottles are no good for fizzy drinks – the gas particles can diffuse through the plastic bottle, so the drink would still go flat.

5 Draw diagrams to show:
   a) a beaker of water with a spoon of Bovril in it
   b) what the beaker would look like if you left it for 5 minutes without stirring
   c) what the beaker would look like if you stirred the Bovril into the water.

6 Which of these are examples of diffusion? Explain your answer in each case:
   A You can smell the aroma of coffee when you open a new jar of granules.
   B You stir your tea to get the sugar to dissolve.
   C A breeze is blowing and you smell the cooking from a barbecue next door.
   D A baby has a smelly nappy. You can smell it from across the room.

You should know...
- What diffusion is.
- Diffusion occurs because particles in a substance are always moving.
- Why diffusion is faster in gases than liquids.

What can forces do?

Our life is full of **forces**. We cannot see them but we can see how they affect things. Forces can change the **shape** of something, its **speed**, or the **direction** that it is moving in.

 1 Write down three ways in which a force can affect an object.

Forces are either pushes or pulls. These pictures show some changes caused by forces.

Many forces need to touch an object before they can affect it. These are called **contact forces**. For example, when you throw a ball, you need to touch the ball to put a force on it. When you go down a steep hill on a bicycle, the brakes need to touch the wheel to produce a force called **friction** to slow you down.

 2 Look at the pictures above. For each picture, write down:
a) whether the force is a push or a pull
b) whether the force is changing the shape, speed or direction.

friction from brakes

air resistance

water resistance

Upthrust

Friction happens when two things rub against each other.

The friction caused when something moves through air is called **air resistance**.

The friction caused when something moves through water is called **water resistance**.

Upthrust pushes things up. Even the chair you are sitting on gives you upthrust!

 3 Look at the three pictures showing different types of friction. For each picture write down what two things are rubbing against each other to make the friction.

Air resistance and water resistance are sometimes called **drag**

Some forces can affect an object from a distance. These are called **non-contact forces**.

Gravity pulls everything downwards towards the centre of the Earth.

Static electricity can attract charged things.

Magnets have **magnetism**, which attracts objects made of iron.

 4 Write down the names of three contact forces.

5 Write down the names of three non-contact forces.

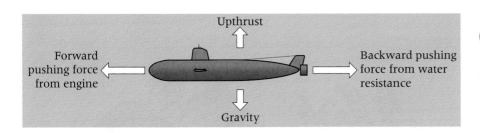

6 Draw a picture of yourself sitting in a chair. Put two labelled arrows on it to show the forces.

Sometimes there are a lot of forces acting on something. There are four forces acting on this submarine.

Forces are all around us and affect everything we do. There is a force from the boy's hand when he is throwing the ball. The force changes the speed of the ball

gravity

The force of gravity is pulling this ball downwards

There is a force from the girl's hands when she catches the ball. The force slows the ball down

gravity

gravity

You should know...

- Forces can change the shape, speed or direction of things.
- The names of contact and non-contact forces.

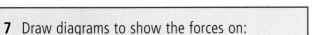 **7** Draw diagrams to show the forces on:
a) a girl on a skateboard going down a hill
b) a boy swimming.

How do forces change the speed of things?

Forces can be large or small. They can work together or they can work against each other.

Two forces work against each other if they are in opposite directions. If the two forces are the same size, nothing will happen. The forces are **balanced**.

If one of the forces is stronger than the other, something will start to move. The forces are **unbalanced**.

Unbalanced forces will make something go faster or slower. They may make something start to move or stop moving. Unbalanced forces can also make things change the direction they are moving in.

? **1** Look at the pictures.
What happens when:
a) both teams push with the same force
b) one team pushes with more force than the other?

2 What will these unbalanced forces do:
a) the force from a car engine when it sets off from traffic lights
b) the force of friction in the brakes of a bicycle going down a hill
c) the force from a footballer when he heads a ball?

Balanced forces cannot make something start or stop moving, or change its speed. If something is already moving, balanced forces keep it moving at the same speed. The motor scooter is moving at a steady speed. The forward force from the engine is exactly balanced by friction in the wheels and by air resistance.

 3 Are the forces balanced or unbalanced when:
   a) you are sitting in a chair
   b) a car is starting off from traffic lights
   c) an apple is falling off a tree
   d) a duck is floating on a pond?

If there are no forces on something that is moving, it carries on moving at the same speed.

Think about trying to throw a ball across a football pitch. It does not go very far because gravity is pulling it downwards and air resistance is slowing it down.

However, if you could throw the ball in outer space it would not stop. There is no air in space, so there would be no air resistance to slow it down. If something is already moving, it carries on moving unless a force slows it down.

The Earth was moving around the Sun when it was formed. There are no forces in space to slow it down, so it carries on moving around the Sun. It does not need a force to keep it moving.

 4 Copy and complete these sentences:
_____ forces cannot change the _____ of moving things. _____ can change the _____ or _____ that something is moving in.

5 A speed boat needs its engine to keep going at a steady speed:
   a) What is the force trying to slow down the boat?
   b) What would happen to the boat if the engine was turned off?

6 If you try to slide a stone across the floor, it will soon stop:
   a) Why does the stone stop?
   b) It will go further if you slide it on ice. Why?
   c) If there was no friction at all between the moving stone and the ice, what would happen to it?

7 Draw sketches for the three situations in question 2. Draw arrows on your sketches to show all the forces. Write the names of the forces if you can.

You should know…
- **Unbalanced forces can affect the speed of things.**
- **Balanced forces do not change the speed of things.**

How can we measure a force?

Forces can make things change shape. A big force will make something change shape more than a small force.

We measure forces using a **force meter** (also known as a **Newton meter**). A force meter has a spring inside it which can be stretched. The amount of stretch in the spring depends on the size of the force. The units for measuring forces are **newtons (N)**.

A spring is used in a force meter because it is **elastic**. Something that is elastic goes back to its original shape after it has been stretched. Plasticine will also stretch but it is not elastic.

1 Write down three things that you can change the shape of with your hands.

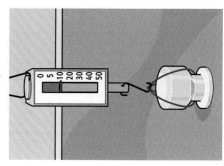

It takes a force of 10 N to open this door

2 What do we use for measuring forces?

3 What are the units for measuring forces?

The **weight** of something is the amount of force with which **gravity** is pulling it down. Weights can be measured with a force meter.

P How could you make your own force meter?
- What elastic object will you use?
- How would you find out how much it stretches with different weights?
- How would you use it to weigh an object?

Robert Hooke (1635–1703) was a famous British scientist who studied how metals behave when they stretch. His work led to the invention of the force meter. However the units for measuring forces were named after his rival and arch enemy, Isaac Newton!

4 a) What word describes something which will go back to its original shape after being stretched?
   b) Why don't we use Plasticine in a force meter?

You should know...
- The units used for measuring forces are newtons (N).
- How a force meter works.

How can things be made stronger?

Sometimes we do not want forces to change things. Buildings and bridges have to be strong enough so that the forces acting on them do not change their shapes too much and break them.

When we want something to be strong, we:
● use a strong material
● use a strong shape.

The type of material used is very important. Plastic objects are cheap to make but can break easily. Bridges are often built out of metal, but never plastic.

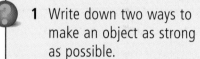

P How could you bridge a gap between two stools with a strip of card?
● Which shapes will you use to build your bridge?
● How much weight will different shapes support?

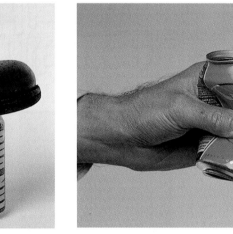

The shape of the object is also very important. A metal soft-drink can is very strong if you apply forces to its ends. You can stand on a can, and it will easily take your weight. However, if you apply the forces to the sides of the can it is not very strong. You can squash it using your fingers. The shape of the can is designed to be strong in only one direction.

?
1 Write down two ways to make an object as strong as possible.

2 Why are soft-drink cans designed to take a lot of weight? (Think about what happens when the cans go from the factory to the shops.)

3 Find pictures of different bridges. Try to explain why stone bridges are usually different shapes from metal bridges.

The shape of these beams makes them very strong. Sometimes holes are cut in part of a beam to make it lighter

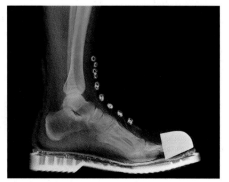

The bones in your feet are arched. Arches are very strong shapes

The body of an aeroplane has to be very strong and light

What is the difference between weight and mass?

Any two objects have a force of attraction between them. This force is called **gravity**. The Earth is so big that its gravity is very strong, and pulls us all towards it.

Your **weight** is the force of gravity pulling on you. Weight is a force, and its units are **newtons (N)**. If you talk about something being 'ten kilograms' you are talking about its mass. At home, we often talk about the weight of things in grams and kilograms. This is not correct. To a scientist, **weight** and **mass** are two different things.

1 a) What is weight?
   b) What are the units for weight?

Mass is the amount of matter which makes something up. The units for measuring mass are **grams (g)** and **kilograms (kg)**.

On Earth, gravity pulls on every kilogram with a force of 10 N. If a bag of apples has a mass of 2 kg, its weight on Earth will be 20 N (multiply 2 kg by 10). If you went to the Moon, where the gravity is not as strong, its mass would still be 2 kg but its weight would only be about 3 N. The gravity on the Moon is only $\frac{1}{6}$ as strong as it is on Earth.

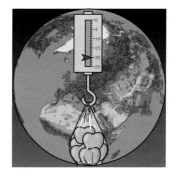

2 Why would you weigh less on the Moon than you do on the Earth?

3 What are the units for measuring mass?

4 a) What is the weight of a 3 kg frozen chicken on the Earth?
   b) What is the mass of the chicken on the Moon?
   c) What is the weight of the chicken on the Moon?

 The 'true' kilogram mass is kept in a safe near Paris. All other kilogram masses are measured against this one.

You should know...

- What the words weight and mass mean.
- What the units used for weight and mass are.

What happens to our weight when we float?

When you are standing on the ground, gravity is pulling you down. An upwards force from the ground stops you sinking into the Earth. This upwards force is called **upthrust**.

When you float in water, you feel that you weigh less. This is because the upthrust of the water pushes up against your weight. You still have weight, but you do not feel it. An object will float when its weight and the upthrust are balanced.

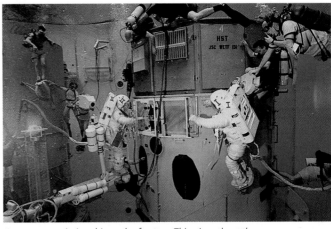

Astronauts train in a big tank of water. This gives them the same 'weightless' feeling that they will get in space

1 a) What two forces affect you when you float?
  b) How do these two forces compare in size?

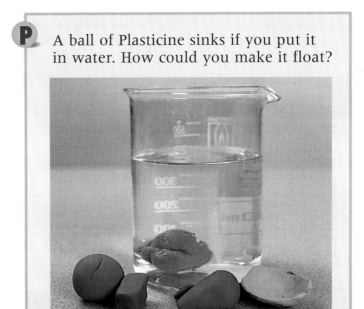

P A ball of Plasticine sinks if you put it in water. How could you make it float?

Whales are mammals that live in the sea. The water helps to support their weight. If a whale gets stranded on a beach it will die because there is no water to support it. Its lungs can be crushed by its own body weight.

2 A whale has a body weight of 600 000 N. What upthrust does it need to float?

3 A hot air balloon is floating in the air. The air gives upthrust:
  a) What are the two forces acting on it?
  b) What can you say about the sizes of the two forces?

You should know...

● What upthrust means.

● Which forces are balanced when something floats.

How can we control friction?

Friction is the force between two touching objects. It can slow things down or make things stand still. The friction between our clothes and a chair stops us from sliding off it. Walking would be very difficult without the friction between our feet and the floor – we would slip and slide everywhere.

 1 Give one example of friction making something stand still.

We can increase friction by using certain materials. Rubber produces a lot of friction which is useful to us. For example, the tyres of a Formula One racing car stop the car from sliding off the road as it speeds round a sharp bend. The rubber mat in a bath stops us from slipping.

We can reduce friction by making surfaces smooth. Skiers wax the bottom of their skis to make them very smooth. This reduces friction and allows them to ski faster.

 2 Why are playground slides made from smooth, polished metal?

Friction is not always useful. Sometimes we want things to move easily. For example, a bicycle would be very difficult to ride if there was too much friction in the axles.

Oil and grease help to reduce friction. Adding oil or grease to something is called **lubrication**. Oil and grease are good **lubricants**.

Rock climbing shoes are made from special rubber that increases friction and gives a good grip

This skier uses special wax to make the bottom of her skis very smooth

 3 a) Why should you oil the axles of a bicycle?
b) Why must you never put oil on the brake blocks of a bicycle?
c) Explain why bicycle brakes do not work very well in the rain.

axle

Friction can also wear things away. The brake pads on a bicycle eventually wear away, and so do car tyres. Parts of your clothes get thinner as friction wears them away.

New wheels for a train

A worn out trian wheel. The metal on this wheel has worn away because of friction between the wheel and the railway lines

4 Why do car owners have to replace their car tyres regularly?

Friction produces heat and noise. If a car engine runs without any oil in it, the large friction between the moving parts inside the engine causes it to overheat and stop working. Rusty door hinges squeak and make a door difficult to open.

Gases and liquids can also cause friction. **Air resistance** and **water resistance** are both kinds of friction.

5 How could you stop a door hinge squeaking?

6 Write down three things that friction can do to a moving object.

7 Write down two things you could do to reduce the friction between two objects.

8 Describe five ways in which friction is useful to you in your everyday life.

P
Young children enjoy playing on slides. Some clothes have more friction than others. How would you find out which sort of material would allow a child to go down a slide fastest?
- What will you use to measure the force of friction?
- How will you make it a fair test?

One of the substances which produces the least friction is a plastic called PTFE. It has a very smooth surface. It is also used to coat non-stick pans. It was discovered by accident by Roy Plunkett in 1938. He found that some of the gases he was using in designs for refrigerators had turned into a solid.

You should know...
- **When friction is useful and when it is not useful.**
- **How to increase friction.**
- **How to reduce friction by lubrication.**

How can we work out how fast something is moving?

Speed is a way of saying how far you travel in a certain time. This time can be a second (s), a minute (min) or an hour (h) or even longer.

To work out a speed, you have to measure a distance and a time. You can calculate the speed using this formula:

$$\text{speed} = \frac{\text{distance}}{\text{time}}$$

The units you use for speed depend on the measurements you make. For instance, if a car travels 200 miles in 4 hours, its speed would be in miles per hour (mph).

 1 How fast is the car going?

2 A bus travelled 60 km in 2 hours.
  a) What units would you use for its speed?
  b) What was its speed?

3 You are growing a little taller each year. What units could you use to measure how fast you are growing?

Michael Johnson ran the 200 m in 19.32 seconds.

First, write down the formula:

$$\text{speed} = \frac{\text{distance}}{\text{time}} \quad \text{or speed distance} \div \text{time}$$

Then put in the numbers:

$$\text{speed} = \frac{200\,\text{m}}{19.32\,\text{s}} \quad \text{or speed} = 200\,\text{m} \div 19.32\,\text{s}$$

Then work out the answer (don't forget the units!):

$$= 10.35 \text{ metres per second (m/s)}$$

A bus in town never moves at a steady speed. Instead it slows down, stops to pick up passengers, and then speeds up. It might also have to stop at traffic lights. In this case we work out a **mean** (average) speed for the bus. This is the total distance the bus has driven divided by the time taken for the journey.

 4 A bus travelled a distance of 5 km in 15 min after stopping several times during the trip. What was its mean speed?

P How could you find the average walking speed for your class?
- How would you measure the distance?
- How would you measure the time?

5 Write down three different units that are usually used for speed.

6 It takes you half an hour to walk 2 miles to school. What is your mean walking speed?

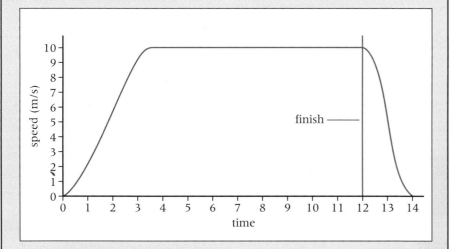

7 The graph shows how the speed of a sprinter changes during a 100 m race:
a) How long did the race last?
b) What is the mean speed of the sprinter?
c) What is the fastest speed recorded on the graph?

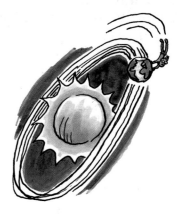

The Earth travels around the Sun at a speed of about 30 000 metres per second. (m/s)

You should know...
- How to calculate the speed of something.
- Different units can be used to measure speed.

Why do we have days, nights and years?

We live on a planet called **Earth**. The Earth is shaped like a **sphere**. The Earth gets heat and light from the **Sun**.

Day and night

The Earth spins on its **axis**. A **day** is the time it takes for one spin. It takes 24 hours for this to happen on Earth.

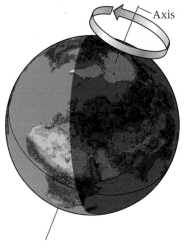

Axis

1 What provides the Earth with heat and light?

2 How long does it take the Earth to spin once round on its axis?

Warning: Never look directly at the Sun – it could damage your eyes.

This side of the Earth is facing the Sun. It is daytime for the people that live here

It is night time on this side of the Earth because it is facing away from the Sun

The Sun seems to move across the sky during the day. It rises in the east and sets in the west. This happens because the Earth is spinning, *not* because the Sun is moving around the Earth.

Shadows move as the Earth spins.
People used to use this idea to tell the time.

A sundial can be used to tell the time

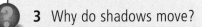

3 Why do shadows move?

The Earth moves around the Sun. The path it takes is called its **orbit**. The length of time it takes a planet to travel once around the Sun is called a **year**.

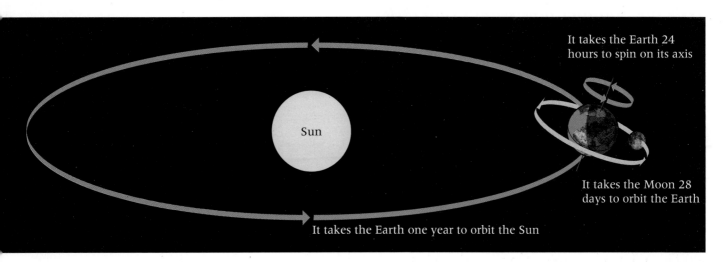

It takes the Earth 24 hours to spin on its axis

Sun

It takes the Moon 28 days to orbit the Earth

It takes the Earth one year to orbit the Sun

An Earth year is 365.25 days long. Our calendar has 365 days in every year, so every four years there is an extra day to make up the lost time. This day is added to the end of February in a **leap year**.

4 What is a year?

5 What is a leap year?

The Moon

A **satellite** is something that goes around a planet. The Moon is a natural satellite of the Earth. It orbits (goes around) the Earth once every 28 days. This is called a **lunar month**.

6 What is a satellite?

7 How long is an Earth day?

8 How long is an Earth year?

9 What is a lunar month?

You should know...

● The Earth gets heat and light from the Sun.

● The Earth spins on its axis.

● The Earth orbits around the Sun.

● What day, year and leap year mean.

● The Moon is a natural satellite of the Earth.

Why are summer and winter different?

The weather in Britain is very different at different times of the year.

Summer

Winter

These photos show the same place in summer and winter

1 Describe the differences between summer and winter for:
   a) the length of daylight
   b) the temperature.

These changes happen because the Earth's axis is tilted.

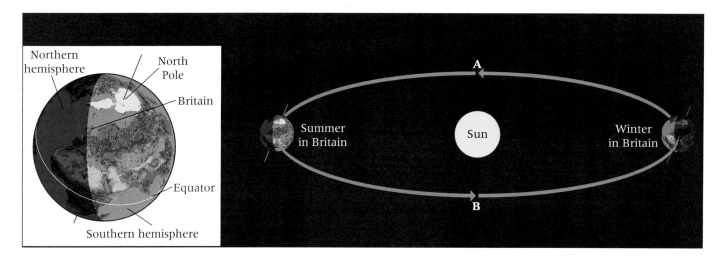

The Earth has two halves or **hemispheres**. Britain is in the **northern hemisphere**. When the northern hemisphere is tilted towards the Sun it is summer in Britain. The Sun is high in the sky at midday, and days are longer than nights.

When the northern hemisphere is tilted away from the Sun it is winter in Britain. The Sun is not very high in the sky at midday, and nights are longer than days.

2 Explain what a hemisphere is.

3 Look at the diagram:
   a) What season will it be when the Earth is at position A?
   b) What season will it be when the Earth is at position B?

4 Look carefully at this picture. Explain why days are longer than nights in summer.

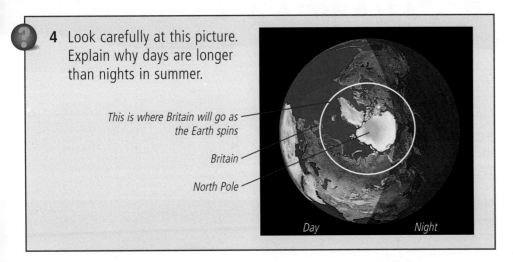

This is where Britain will go as the Earth spins

Britain

North Pole

Day   Night

The Sun feels hotter in the summer than it does in the winter. Some people think that this is because the Earth is closer to the Sun in summer, but this is not true.

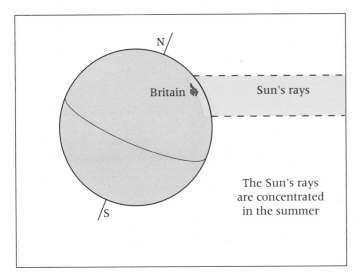

N

Britain   Sun's rays

S

The Sun's rays are concentrated in the summer

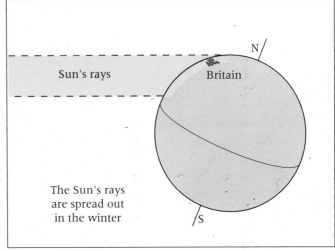

N

Sun's rays   Britain

S

The Sun's rays are spread out in the winter

The Sun feels hotter in the summer because it is higher in the sky. The heat from the Sun is more concentrated in the summer. Summer days are also warmer than winter days because the Sun is shining for longer, and has more time to warm up the air and the ground.

5 Draw a diagram looking at the Earth from above the North Pole in winter (similar to the one at the top of this page). Use your diagram to help you to explain why nights are longer than days in winter.

6 Australia is on the opposite side of the Earth to Britain. Which season is it in Australia when it is summer in Britain?

7 If you were near the North Pole, how long would daylight last in summer? What would happen in winter?

8 If you live near the equator the Sun always feels hotter than it does in Britain. Use a diagram to help you to explain why.

You should know...
- **The differences between summer and winter**
- **We have seasons because the Earth's axis is tilted.**
- **The northern hemisphere is tilted towards the Sun in the summer.**

What is the Solar System?

The Earth is not the only planet orbiting around the Sun. There are nine planets in the **Solar System**, and thousands of **asteroids** (small lumps of rock). Most of the planets have **moons** orbiting around them.

You can remember the order of the planets using this sentence: 'My Very Easy Method Just Sums Up Nine Planets'. This drawing is not to scale

The four planets closest to the Sun are known as the **inner planets**. They are rocky planets. The other planets are the **outer planets**. Except for Pluto, the outer planets are made of gas. The Earth is the only planet that has living things on it. The other planets are too hot or too cold.

 1 Write down the names of the inner planets, starting with the one closest to the Sun.

2 Name the planets that are made of gas?

When you look at the sky on a clear night you can see lots of **stars**. Stars are huge balls of gas that give out large amounts of light and heat energy. The Sun is a star. The stars you see at night do not seem very bright because they are much further away than the Sun.

 3 What is a star?

4 Why does the Sun look much brighter than the other stars?

You can sometimes see planets in the night sky. We can see planets because they reflect light from the Sun. They do not make their own light. Planets look brighter than stars because they are much closer to the Earth.

 5 Why do planets look like stars in the night sky?

A Polish astronomer called Copernicus (1473–1543) suggested that the planets went around the Sun. Until that time people thought that everything went around the Earth. In 1610 another astronomer called Galileo proved that Copernicus was correct by using one of the first telescopes. The Christian church believed that the Earth was at the centre of the Solar System, and Galileo was arrested when he wrote about his theory.

Planet	Distance from Sun (million km)	Mean surface temperature (°C)
Mercury	58	170
Venus	108	460
Earth	150	15
Mars	228	−50
Jupiter	778	−143
Saturn	1427	−195
Uranus	2870	−201
Neptune	4497	−220
Pluto	5913	−205

Uranus

Pluto

Neptune

6 a) Draw a bar chart showing the mean temperature of each planet.
b) Describe the pattern you can see from your graph.
c) The asteroids are about 400 million km from the Sun. Use your graph to estimate the mean temperature on an asteroid.
d) One planet does not fit the pattern on the graph. Find out why this planet does not follow the pattern.

Model Sun

Model Moon

Model Earth

The Sun is enormous compared with the planets. This model in Geneva represents the Sun and the Earth to the correct scale. The model of the Earth is 4.5 cm in diameter, the model of the Sun is 4.5 m in diameter and is 450 m away.

You should know...

- A solar system contains a star at the centre and other objects orbiting the star.

- A planet is a large object that orbits around a star.

- The Sun is at the centre of our Solar System, and there are nine planets.

Why does the shape of the Moon seem to change?

The Moon is much smaller than the Earth. Like the planets, it does not produce its own light. We can only see the Moon because it reflects sunlight back towards the Earth.

1 How big is the Moon compared with the Earth?

2 How are we able to see the Moon?

Moon

This half of the moon is lit by the sun

Sun

Earth

From Earth the Moon looks like this

The shape of the Moon seems to change as it orbits the Earth. The different shapes are called **phases of the Moon**. Half of the Moon is always lit by the Sun, but we cannot always see all of the lit part.

When the Moon looks like a full circle it is called a **full moon**. It takes 28 days for the Moon to orbit the Earth once. It is 28 days, or one lunar month, between one full moon and the next.

The Moon is the Earth's only natural satellite. It has no atmosphere. This means there is no air, no wind and no rain. There is no life on the Moon.

3 How many days are there between one full moon and the next?

4 What would humans need to take with them to live on the Moon?

This is a footprint left by one of the Apollo astronauts. It will never be blown away

You should know...

● We see the Moon because it reflects sunlight.

● The shape of the Moon seems to change as it moves around the Earth.

How far away are the stars?

If you look carefully at the stars you can see patterns, called **constellations**. Long ago people thought that gods lived in the sky, and named some of the patterns after gods or animals.

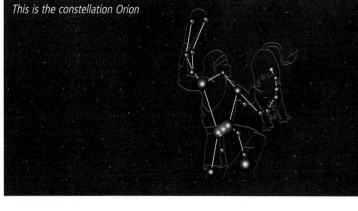
This is the constellation Orion

 1 What is a constellation?

The distances between stars are so large that they are hard to imagine. Scientists measure these distances in **light years**. One light year is the distance travelled by light in one year. It works out as 10 000 000 000 000 000 km (ten thousand million million km).

The nearest star to the Sun is called Proxima Centauri. It is 4.22 light years away.

 2 Does a 'light year' measure distance or time?

3 How long would it take light from the Sun to get to Proxima Centauri?

A large group of stars is called a **galaxy**. The Sun is in a galaxy called the **Milky Way**. There are millions of other galaxies, and each of these galaxies contains millions of stars. All these galaxies make up the **Universe**.

 Sailors used to use stars to navigate their ships. This is a sextant. It can be pointed at certain stars to find the position of a ship.

The bright band of stars is part of the Milky Way. It is the part of our galaxy that we can see from Earth

Scientists think that our galaxy looks something like this

 4 What is a galaxy?

5 Write these things in order, starting with the smallest and ending with the largest:
Earth   Universe   Moon   Sun
asteroid   Solar System   galaxy

You should know...

● **What the words constellation, galaxy, Milky Way and Universe mean.**

What is gravity?

When any two objects are near each other they produce a tiny force which tries to pull them together. This force is called **gravity**. The bigger the object, the stronger the force it produces.

Even your body attracts things around you by gravity, but the force you produce is too small for you to notice. The Earth is enormous, so it produces a large force. This force pulls you towards the centre of the Earth.

> **?** **1** Which produces the stronger force of gravity – large or small objects?

> **?** **2** Why is the skydiver falling towards the Earth?

The hard ground you stand on stops you from sinking any further towards the centre of the Earth. The force of gravity pulling on you is your weight, and is measured in newtons (N).

600N

The Moon is not as large as the Earth, but it is still big enough to produce a large force of gravity.

If you could go to the Moon your mass would stay the same but your weight would be less.

100N

> **?** **3** Would the force of gravity on the Moon be bigger or smaller than the force of gravity on Earth? Explain your answer.

The Moon's gravity pulls the water in the oceans towards it. There is a high tide where there is more water than normal. In the places where the water has been pulled away there is a low tide.

> **?** **4** What causes the tides?

> **You should know...**
> ● **Big objects have a stronger force of gravity than smaller objects.**

How does gravity affect the planets?

The Sun is more than 300 000 times more massive than the Earth. Its gravity is very strong. The Earth is moving around the Sun at approximately 100 000 km/h. If there was no gravity from the Sun the Earth would fly off into space. The Sun's gravity keeps the Earth moving in an **elliptical** (oval) orbit around the Sun.

1 What stops the Earth from moving away from the Sun?

Gravity gets weaker when the two objects attracting each other are a long way apart. Pluto is 40 times further from the Sun than the Earth is. The Sun's gravitational pull on Pluto is much weaker than on the Earth, but it is still strong enough to keep Pluto in its orbit.

2 On which planet in the Solar System would the Sun's gravity be strongest?

The Earth's gravity keeps the Moon in its orbit. Most of the other planets in the Solar System also have moons.

Beyond the Solar System

Gravity does not stop outside the Solar System. There is a force of attraction between all the stars in the Galaxy. This holds the Galaxy together. Even different galaxies attract each other. There is a force of gravity everywhere in the Universe, although it is very weak in some places.

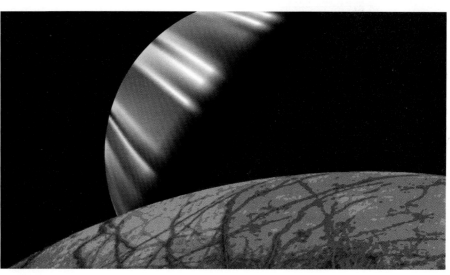
This is how Jupiter might look from from the surface of one of its moons

Galaxies can have different shapes

3 Some galaxies are found in groups. What keeps these groups of galaxies together?

You should know...

- **The Sun's gravity keeps the planets in orbit around the Sun.**
- **There is a force of gravity everywhere in the Universe.**

How do we know what the other planets are like?

Early scientists studied the planets and stars using telescopes. However we did not get a really good idea of what the planets looked like until telescopes and cameras went into space.

Here are some of the main events in our exploration of space:

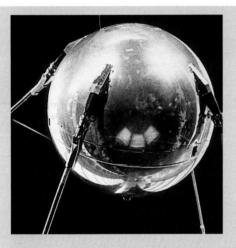

1957 The Russians were the first people to send an object into orbit around the Earth. This was a tiny satellite called Sputnik 1. It sent a simple 'beep' signal from space that could be heard by using a radio on Earth.

1961 A Russian cosmonaut called Yuri Gagarin was the first person to travel in space. He orbited the planet in a tiny space capsule called Vostok 1. He was greeted as a hero on his return to Earth.

1969 The Americans won the race to the Moon with the Apollo 11 mission. Neil Armstrong and Buzz Aldrin were the first human beings to walk on the Moon.

1970 Venera 7 landed on the surface of Venus and sent information back to Russia. The Venera 7 capsule was the first man-made object to send information from the surface of another planet. 'Venera' means 'Venus'.

1973 An unmanned space probe called Pioneer 10 was launched. It carries a written message in case an extra-terrestrial civilisation finds it. It is now outside the Solar System, heading for the stars.

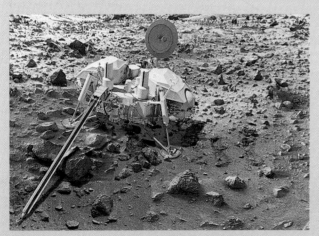

1976 The Viking 1 space probe landed on Mars and sent back the first photograph taken on the surface of the 'Red Planet'. Viking 1 did not find any life on Mars.

1981 The first space shuttle was launched. This was the first space vehicle designed to be re-used for further trips into space.

1986 The Mir space station was launched by the Russians. This laboratory in the sky was used by scientists from many countries for more than 10 years. It allowed them to carry out experiments without being affected by gravity.

1990 The Hubble Space Telescope was launched into Earth orbit. One of the main parts of the telescope was faulty, and had to be repaired by astronauts.

1995 Instruments on the Hubble Space Telescope discovered that Europa, one of the moons of Jupiter, has oxygen in its atmosphere. Europa is the first moon ever found to have oxygen in its atmosphere.

1997 The Pathfinder space probe landed on Mars. It carried a tiny robot vehicle called 'Sojourner' which examined the surface of Mars and sent information back to Earth.

---

1   How did people first investigate the planets?

2   What was the first object to be sent into space?

3   What is the furthest place in the Solar System that humans have visited?

4   a) Who was the first person in space?
    b) Who were the first people to walk on the Moon?

5   The Hubble telescope is in orbit around the Earth. Why would a telescope in orbit be able to take better pictures than a telescope on Earth?

6   The space probes on this page are not the only ones that have explored space. Find out about the following space probes, where they went and what they found out:
    a) Voyager 1 and 2
    b) Galileo.

Why is energy needed?

Nothing would happen without energy. Energy is needed to make things move, to provide heat and light, and to keep living things alive. There are many different forms of energy. This photograph shows some examples of **energy in action**.

Moving objects have **kinetic** (moving) **energy**. The faster something moves, the more kinetic energy it has.

Electrical energy can be used to provide light, sound and kinetic energy. It can also provide heat energy to cook food.

Noisy things and people produce **sound energy.**

The Sun provides us with both **heat energy** and **light energy**. Light bulbs can also provide heat and light.

1 Write a list of the five kinds of energy in action.

2 Write down three things which:
   a) have kinetic energy
   b) give out light and heat energy
   c) produce sound energy
   d) use electrical energy.

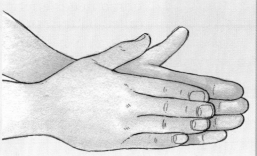

P Rub the palms of your hands together. Describe what happens and say which types of energy are involved. (*Hint*: There are three kinds of energy in action.)

3 Copy and complete this table to show five things from your home that use energy. Next to each object write down the kinds of energy that it uses or produces.

Object	Forms of energy
television	electrical, light, sound, heat

4 Which kinds of energy in action can you see in this photograph? Give at least one example of each kind of energy.

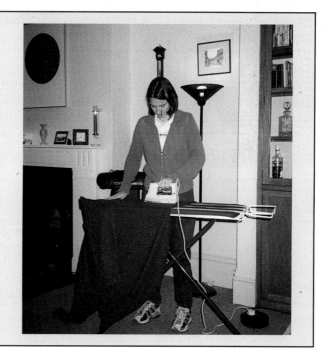

You should know…
● **Why we need energy.**
● **Heat, light, sound, kinetic and electrical are all forms of energy in action.**

How can energy be stored?

Some energy can be stored. For example, this carnival float needs stored energy from diesel so that it can move. Your body needs stored energy so that you can move and keep warm, and to keep your body working. A personal stereo needs energy stored in **cells** (sometimes called batteries).

Stored energy is called **potential energy**. The potential energy in food, cells and fuels like petrol and diesel is called **chemical energy**.

1 Copy and complete these sentences:

The kind of _____ energy found in food is called _____ energy. Chemical energy is also found in _____ and _____ .

Anything which can move downwards contains a store of energy. This is called **gravitational potential energy**, and is due to gravity. The diver has gravitational potential energy because she can move downwards. Even a pen balanced on the table has gravitational potential energy because it could fall off.

2 Why does the diver have gravitational potential energy?

Stretched elastic bands can store energy. This kind of potential energy is called **strain energy**. Strain energy is stored whenever something is stretched, bent or squashed. For example, when you wind up a clockwork toy you store strain energy in the spring. This energy is released when the spring unwinds and goes back to its original shape.

3 Name two objects which contain strain energy.

In some countries it is difficult to get electricity or it is very expensive. In 1991 Trevor Bayliss invented a wind-up radio to allow people in these areas to listen to the news and music.

4 The bungee jumper has strain energy and gravitational potential energy. Which photo shows the bungee jumper with the most:

a) strain energy

b) gravitational potential energy?

Nuclear (or **atomic**) **energy** is stored in particles that make up certain metals (for example, uranium). Nuclear power stations use this energy to produce heat, which is used to produce electricity. The Sun also contains a store of nuclear energy which it uses to produce heat and light.

 David Kirke, from Oxford University, invented bungee jumping. He got the idea from Pentecost Island where teenagers tie long vines to their feet and leap from treetops.

Measuring energy

The units for measuring energy are **joules** (**J**). 1000 joules are called a **kilojoule** (**kJ**).

P How could you investigate how much chemical energy is stored in different foods?
- How would you measure the energy?
- How could you make your experiment fair?
- What safety rules would you follow?

Nutrition Information		
	Per 100 g	Per Pack
Energy	2358 kJ	472 kJ
	564 kcal	113 kcal
Protein	3.2 g	0.6 g
Carbohydrate	53.2 g	10.6 g
Fat	37.5 g	7.5 g

Food labels show how much chemical energy is stored in the food

5 Copy and complete these sentences:

The units for measuring energy are _____ .

One kilojoule equals _____ joules.

6 Write down the four different forms of stored energy, and give an example of each form.

7 Food and petrol have chemical energy stored in them. Write down four other things that store chemical energy.

You should know...
- **Stored energy is called potential energy.**
- **The four different forms of stored energy.**

Is your body a machine?

Energy must be changed to be useful. Your body uses the chemical energy stored in food and changes it to other forms of energy.

The snow boarder needs the chemical energy stored in food. He uses some of this energy to keep warm and to stay alive. Some of the energy is stored in his body.

Some of the energy from his food is changed to kinetic energy as he climbs the mountain. As he gets higher, his kinetic energy is also changed to gravitational potential energy.

As he is going down the mountain, his gravitational potential energy is being changed back into kinetic energy.

When he stops, his kinetic energy is converted into sound and heat energy.

This energy flow diagram shows the main energy changes taking place.

chemical energy	kinetic energy	gravitational potential energy	kinetic energy	heat and sound energy
in food	*as he climbs the mountain*	*at the top of the mountain*	*as he slides down the mountain*	*when he has stopped*

1 a) Where does the snow boarder get the energy to climb the mountain?

b) What kind of energy does he have at the top of the mountain?

2 Draw an energy flow diagram like the one above to show the energy changes for a runner running up a hill.

Anything that changes energy is a **machine**. Machines always waste some energy.

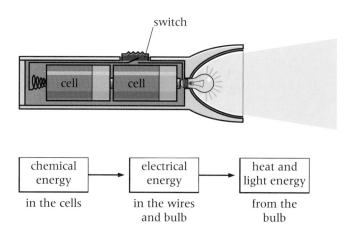

The heat energy that the torch produces is not useful. It is wasted energy.

Energy cannot be made or destroyed, but it can be changed from one form to another. This is known as the **law of conservation of energy**.

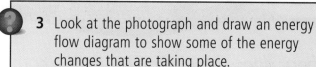

3 Look at the photograph and draw an energy flow diagram to show some of the energy changes that are taking place.

4 a) What form of useful energy does the torch produce?
b) What form of wasted energy does it produce?

5 a) What form of useful energy does a hair dryer produce?
b) What form of wasted energy does it produce?

6 Copy and complete this sentence:

The law of conservation of _____ says that energy can never be _____ or _____, it can only be _____ from one form to another.

7 A torch uses 100 J of stored energy. If 70 J of energy is wasted as heat, how much energy comes out of the torch as light?

8 Draw an energy flow diagram to show the energy changes which take place when you pedal a bicycle. Show useful and wasted energies on your diagram.

9 Describe a day at the go-cart track. Mention as many different energy changes as you can in your story.

You should know...

- Energy can be changed from one form to another.

- Things that change energy from one form to another are called machines.

- Some energy changes produce useful energy, but some energy is wasted.

- Energy is never created or destroyed.

Where does the energy originally come from?

Nearly all the energy we use originally came from the Sun. Heat and light from the Sun provide us with energy directly.

> **1** Where do animals get their energy from?

Sunlight also provides the energy for plants to grow. Light energy from the Sun is used to power **photosynthesis** in plants. This process changes carbon dioxide and water into sugar.

Coal, oil and gas were formed from the remains of dead plants and animals. The energy in these fuels came from the bodies of the plants and animals. The animals got their energy from the plants that they ate, and the plants got their energy from the Sun.

> **2** If you eat a bowl of cornflakes with milk for breakfast, the energy in it originally came from the Sun. Describe how the energy got into your breakfast without using a diagram.

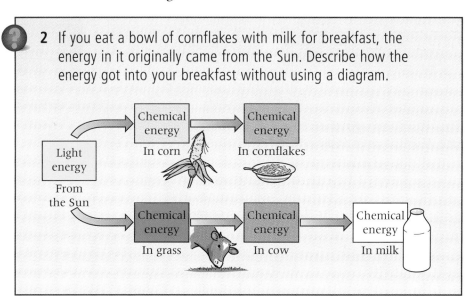

This television uses solar power

> **!** *The Sun keeps the Earth warm. In recent years people have been adding more carbon dioxide and other gases to the atmosphere. These are keeping some of the Sun's heat in and causing the Earth to warm up more than it should. This is known as the greenhouse effect, or global warming.*

People in remote places use solar power for heating water and for making electricity. It is usually difficult to get electrical cables to these places. It is much easier and cheaper to use solar power instead.

Some sources of energy do not come from the Sun. **Nuclear energy**, **geothermal power** (energy from hot rocks deep underground) and energy obtained from tides (**tidal power**) are the only sources of energy that do **not** depend on the Sun.

> **3** What is solar power used for?
>
> **4** a) What are the advantages of using solar power?
>   b) What are the disadvantages?
>
> **5** Bunsen burners use chemical energy stored in methane gas. Explain where this energy came from originally, and how it came to be stored in the gas.
>
> **6** Which sources of energy do not come from the Sun?

What is the difference between heat and temperature?

Heat is a form of energy, so the units for measuring it are joules. When you heat something its temperature usually rises, but heat energy and temperature are not the same thing.

Temperature is a way of saying how hot something is. It can also tell us which way heat energy will flow.

Heat energy flows from something with a higher temperature to something with a lower temperature.

Heat energy flows from the flame to the metal, because the flame has a higher temperature than the metal.

1 What are the units for measuring temperature?

2 a) You can blow on a hot drink to help it to cool down faster. Why does this work?
b) On a cold day you can blow on your fingers to warm them up. Why does this work?

P How could you find out how much the temperature rises in different volumes of water, if you gave each one the same amount of heat?
- How much water would you use in each beaker?
- How could you make it a fair test?

It took 336 kJ of energy to boil the water in this kettle.

The same amount of energy would heat the water in this paddling pool by less than 1°C.

3 If you only want to make one cup of coffee, how much water should you put in the kettle? Explain your answer.

In 1742 Anders Celsius (1701–1744) invented he scale of 0 to 100 that we use on most thermometers today. His first version of the scale had the boiling point of water as 0 degrees, and the freezing point at 100 degrees! The modern unit of temperature (degrees celsius) is named after him.

You should know...
- Heat energy flows from things at a high temperature to things at a lower temperature.
- Heat energy and temperature are not the same.

How does heat travel through solids?

A **conductor** is something that lets energy flow through it. When heat energy travels through solids, this is called **conduction**. Some materials are better heat conductors than others. A poor heat conductor is called a heat **insulator**.

1 Copy these sentences and fill in the gaps: Heat travels through _____ by _____ . Materials that do not let heat travel through them easily are called _____ .

How could you find out which materials are good conductors of heat?
- Which materials could you test?
- How could you find out if they conduct heat well?
- How would you make your investigation fair?

Metals are good heat conductors. Wood and plastic are heat insulators. Air is also a heat insulator.

A saucepan is made of metal because it is a good conductor of heat. Saucepan handles are often made of wood or plastic because they are good insulators of heat.

Central heating radiators are made of metal so that the heat can be conducted from the hot water inside them to the air in the room.

2 a) Why does a saucepan need to be made from a material that is a good conductor?

b) Why are saucepan handles made from insulating materials?

It takes about 70 kJ to heat one mug of water. This is the same as the amount of sound energy produced if you shouted continuously for 8 years, 7 months and 6 days.

The material on the outside of the space shuttle is a good heat insulator. When the shuttle is flying back to Earth the temperature can get as high as 1600 °C

Trapped air is a good heat insulator. For example, feathers trap air and keep birds warm. We use feathers in duvets to keep us warm in bed.

3 Why is a duvet a good heat insulator?

4 Sort the following materials into heat conductors and heat insulators:

| wool | plastic | aluminium foil |
| wood | copper | air |

Air is only a good heat insulator if it cannot move. The heat from your body warms up the air around you. If it is windy, this warm air gets blown away so more heat is taken from your body to heat up the cooler air. You feel much colder on a windy day than you would on a day when there was no breeze. This effect is known as **wind chill**.

Wind speed (km/h)	Wind chill (°C)
10	−3
20	−9
30	−13
40	−15
50	−17

5 This table shows the wind chill for different wind speeds. For example, if the wind was blowing at 10 km/h you would feel 3 °C colder than the actual air temperature:
  a) Plot a graph with wind speed on the horizontal axis.
  b) What is the wind chill if the wind is 20 km/h?
  c) If the wind was blowing at 20 km/h and the actual air temperature was 10 °C, how cold would it feel?
  d) Use your graph to work out how cold it would feel if the wind was 25 km/h and the air temperature was 0 °C.

6 If you pick up a metal spoon it always feels colder than a wooden one. Explain why you think this happens.

You should know...

- Heat travels through solids by heat conduction.

- Metals are good heat conductors – they let heat energy flow through them easily.

- Poor heat conductors are called heat insulators.

- Trapped air is a good heat insulator.

How does heat travel through liquids, gases and space?

When a liquid is heated, the heated part rises and cooler liquid moves in to replace it. This creates a flow which is called a **convection current**.

Convection also happens in gases. Convection can cause winds to blow. During the day the land warms up more quickly than the sea. This means that the air above the land warms up too. The warm air rises and sets up a convection current. Cool breezes blow in from the sea.

The air above the land warms up and rises

The land warms up

Cool air from the sea blows in

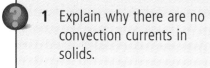

1 Explain why there are no convection currents in solids.

Convection spreads heat energy from hotter areas to cooler areas. For example, a hot drink is cooled by convection currents. The air above the drink is warmed by the drink and rises. The warm air takes some heat energy away from the drink. Cooler air comes in as the warm air rises and absorbs more heat from the drink.

The drink is also cooled by some of the hot liquid turning into a gas. This is called **evaporation**.

2 Why does blowing on a hot drink help to cool it down?

3 Why does air have to be trapped to make it a good heat insulator?

P How could you investigate if the trapped air in bubble wrap acts as a heat insulator?
- How could you find out if heat travels through the bubble wrap?
- How could you make it a fair test?

In space there is nothing to carry a convection current. There is also nothing to conduct energy to the Earth, but the Sun still warms us. The energy from the Sun travels to the Earth by **radiation**. Radiation is heat that travels without needing any substance to go through. All hot objects give off radiation. Radiation can travel through transparent things and through space.

4 How does heat travel to you if you:
   a) stand close to a radiator
   b) touch the radiator
   c) stand at the other end of the room?

Shiny materials reflect radiation. When a baby is born prematurely it is often wrapped in foil. This stops heat escaping from its body and keeps it warm.

Our bodies are warmer than our surroundings. Special cameras can be used to find people who are trapped in wreckage or lost on a mountain.

A vacuum flask can keep hot liquids hot. It can also keep cold liquids cold. This is because it stops nearly all heat energy going into or out of the liquid.

5 The part of a vacuum flask that holds liquids is made of glass:
   a) How does heat travel through solids?
   b) Is glass a good or bad conductor of heat?

There are two layers of glass with a **vacuum** between them. A vacuum is empty space – there is no air in a vacuum. The layers of glass are covered in silver-coloured paint.

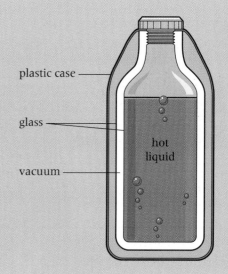
plastic case
glass
hot liquid
vacuum

6 a) How does heat travel through a vacuum?
   b) Why is the glass covered in silver paint?

7 Explain why heat cannot travel through the vacuum flask by conduction.

8 Explain why heat cannot travel through the vacuum flask by convection.

9 Explain why not much heat can travel through the flask by radiation.

You should know...
- **Convection currents carry heat energy in liquids and gases.**
- **Heat can travel through transparent objects and space by radiation.**
- **Shiny materials reflect radiation.**

What are fossil fuels?

A **fuel** is something that can release heat energy. Many fuels contain a store of energy called **chemical energy**. They can be burnt to turn the chemical energy into heat energy. Burning a fuel does not make energy, it only changes it from one form into another. Energy cannot be made or destroyed, only changed from one type into another. This is called the **law of conservation of energy**.

Coal is a common fuel. It was formed many millions of years ago from plants. When the plants died, they became buried in mud which stopped them from rotting away. Organisms that are trapped in mud and do not rot away completely are called **fossils**. More layers of the mud squashed down on the fossils. This squashing, together with heat from inside the Earth, turned the mud into rock and the plant fossils into coal. Coal is called a **fossil fuel**.

 1 What is a fuel?

2 What is the law of conservation of energy?

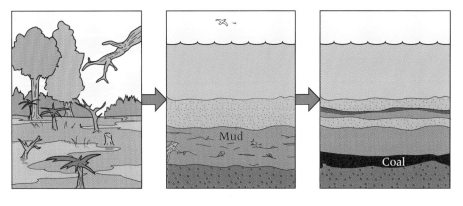

! Fossils of prehistoric plants can often be found in lumps of coal.

Oil and **natural gas** are also fossil fuels. They formed from animals that lived millions of years ago. The animals fell to the sea bed when they died and got buried in mud and sand. They formed fossils. More layers of mud and sand fell on top of the fossils and squashed them, turning them into 'crude' oil and natural gas. The oil and natural gas are often pushed upwards by underground pressure but get stuck under a layer of rock (called 'caprock') which will not let them through.

 3 Why is coal called a fossil fuel?

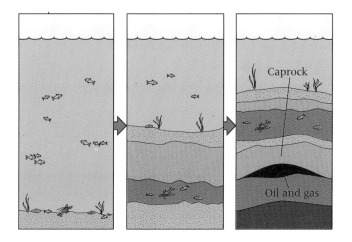

4 a) Write down two similarities between the formation of coal and oil.

b) Write down two differences.

 There are many types of fuel. How would you find out which fuel is best for heating water?
- How would you get your fuels to burn?
- What would you measure?
- How would you make this a fair test?
- How would you make sure your experiment was done safely?

Fossil fuels are described as **non-renewable**. It takes many millions of years for them to form and so our supplies will eventually run out. We cannot renew our supplies of them. There is only enough oil to last another 40 years but enough coal to last about 225 years.

 5 What is a non-renewable fuel?

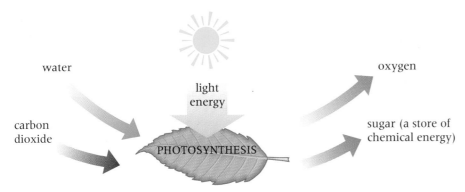

water

light energy

oxygen

carbon dioxide

PHOTOSYNTHESIS

sugar (a store of chemical energy)

Plants trap sunlight for **photosynthesis**. This process turns light energy into chemical energy. Plants therefore contain chemical energy. When an animal eats a plant, it takes in the plant's chemical energy. The chemical energy in a fossil fuel comes from the chemical energy in the dead plants and animals that made it. This energy originally came from the Sun.

 6 Write down the names of three fossil fuels.

7 A friend of yours says, 'All my energy comes from the Sun.' Explain why he is right.

8 Copy and complete these sentences:
When you burn a fuel, chemical energy is turned into _____ energy. The chemical energy in the fuel is originally from the _____ . This energy was trapped by plants using the process of _____ . This process changes _____ energy into _____ energy.

9 a) Complete this sentence: 'Energy cannot be made or destroyed, only ... .'

b) What law does this sentence describe?

You should know...
- **What fossil fuels are and how they were made.**
- **Chemical energy in fossil fuels originally came from the Sun.**
- **The law of conservation of energy.**

How is electricity produced and transported?

About 20% of the fossil fuels that we produce are used to make **electricity**. Electricity is **generated** in power stations. It flows from the power stations through a series of cables, called the **National Grid**.

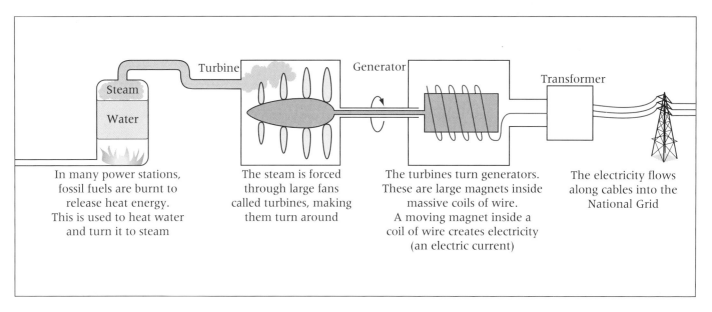

| Steam | Turbine | Generator | Transformer |

In many power stations, fossil fuels are burnt to release heat energy. This is used to heat water and turn it to steam

The steam is forced through large fans called turbines, making them turn around

The turbines turn generators. These are large magnets inside massive coils of wire. A moving magnet inside a coil of wire creates electricity (an electric current)

The electricity flows along cables into the National Grid

1 Where is electricity generated?

2 How does a generator work?

Michael Faraday (1791–1867) discovered in 1831 that an electric current could be produced by moving a magnet inside a coil of wire.

The energy changes in a power station can be shown in an **energy flow diagram**.

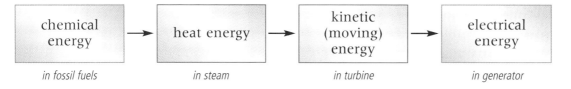

| chemical energy | → | heat energy | → | kinetic (moving) energy | → | electrical energy |

in fossil fuels   *in steam*   *in turbine*   *in generator*

3 What is kinetic energy?

4 Electricity is used in a lamp:
   a) What types of energy does the lamp produce?
   b) Draw an energy flow diagram to show the energy changes.

The National Grid contains many cables hung on pylons or buried underground. Most of the cables are made of **aluminium**. The aluminium is light and allows electricity to get through it easily. Aluminium is a good **electrical conductor**.

The electricity carried by the cables is very dangerous. It would kill you if you touched it. To stop any electricity going through the metal pylons and reaching the ground, the cables are hung on pieces of ceramic (pottery) material. Ceramic materials do not allow electricity to flow through them. They are **electrical insulators**.

5 How does electricity get from power stations to our homes?

6 Why are most of the cables made from aluminium?

7 a) What is an electrical conductor?
  b) What is an electrical insulator?

8 a) Copy and complete this energy flow diagram.

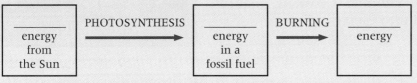

_____ energy from the Sun → PHOTOSYNTHESIS → _____ energy in a fossil fuel → BURNING → _____ energy

  b) Continue the diagram to show the rest of the energy changes in a power station.

9 The diagram shows the inside of a bicycle dynamo. It can produce enough electricity to light up a bicycle light:

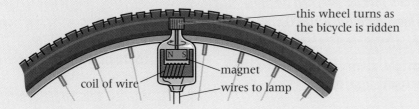

this wheel turns as the bicycle is ridden

coil of wire   magnet   wires to lamp

  a) Explain how it works.
  b) Draw an energy flow diagram to show the energy changes when the dynamo is lighting the lamp.

10 Imagine that there is a plan to build some electricity pylons near your house. What are the arguments for and against such a plan?

The National Grid contains 7000 kilometres of overhead cables and 600 kilometres of underground cables. That is enough cable to stretch from England to India.

You should know...

● **How electricity is produced and how it gets to our homes.**

What is a cell and how does it work?

Electricity that comes to our houses along wires is known as **mains electricity**. However, we often need a source of electricity when we are away from a supply of mains electricity.

 1 What is mains electricity?

Cells can be used instead of mains electricity. Cells are sometimes called batteries. Large cells are used to get cars started. Small ones are used in watches.

Experiments using electricity often use cells because they are safer than using mains electricity. In school, power packs are sometimes used instead of cells. Power packs make mains electricity safer to use.

Cells bought in shops contain dangerous chemicals. You should never try to open one. These chemicals contain a store of chemical energy which is turned into electrical energy.

 2 a) What is a cell?
　　b) What energy change takes place in a cell when it is put into a torch?

Alessandro Volta (1745–1827) spent many years finding out why dead frogs' legs jumped when touched by certain metals. He used what he had learned from these experiments to invent the cell in 1800.

After a while, cells run out of chemical energy. They are said to go flat. Most flat cells cannot be used again.

Some cells are **rechargeable**. They can be recharged by putting them in a charger, connected to mains electricity.

You should know...
- **Cells can be used as a source of electricity.**

 P Very simple cells can be made using two pieces of metal dipped into a fruit juice.
- How would you find out which fruit juice worked best?
- What would you look for?

 3 a) Why should cells never be opened?
　　b) Why do you think it is important to get rid of a 'flat' cell carefully?

4 A wound up spring contains a store of energy called strain energy. This strain energy can be used to make a radio work. Draw an energy flow diagram to show what happens when a wind-up radio is switched on.

What is voltage?

Everything is made of very small particles. Each of these particles contains some **electrical charges**. If these are made to move, you get an **electrical current**. The charges cannot move through electrical **insulators** but they can go through **conductors**.

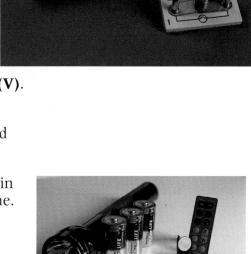

The photograph shows an electrical circuit. The charges are too small to see but we know that they are moving because the lamp is glowing. There is an electrical current.

The cell pushes the current around the circuit. The amount of pushing that it does is called the **voltage**, measured in **volts (V)**.

Cells bought in shops are often 1.5 volts. Using one cell provides 1.5 volts, using two provides 3 volts and so on. Some things need small voltages, others need much bigger voltages.

Voltages can be changed using a **transformer**. Mains electricity in our homes is 230 volts, which is enough to kill or injure someone. A portable stereo, which can use mains electricity, contains a transformer which changes the mains voltage to 9 volts.

The National Grid uses transformers. Power stations produce electricity at about 25 000 volts. This is turned into 444 000 volts for the National Grid. High voltages are used because they do not heat up the cables as much as low voltages. Transformers lower this voltage again close to where the electricity is needed. These transformers are known as electricity substations.

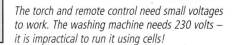

The torch and remote control need small voltages to work. The washing machine needs 230 volts – it is impractical to run it using cells!

> **1** Write down the names of five materials that are electrical insulators and five that are electrical conductors.
>
> **2** a) What is a transformer?
>   b) Why would a factory need more voltage than a house?

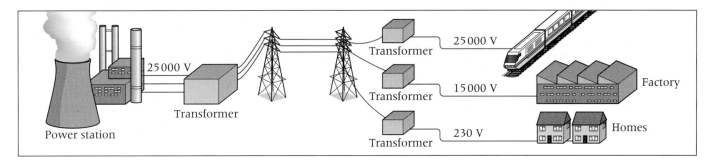

Power station — 25 000 V — Transformer — 25 000 V — Transformer — 15 000 V — Factory — Transformer — 230 V — Homes

What other energy sources are available?

Nuclear power stations use a metal called **uranium**. It is dangerous because it gives off large amounts of **radioactivity**, which can cause cancer. However, the radioactivity can be used to heat water and turn it to steam in a power station.

Uranium was formed when the Earth was formed and so it will eventually run out. Like fossil fuels, once it has been used it cannot be replaced. It is non-renewable.

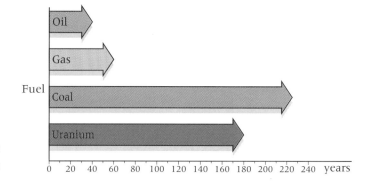

1 What is uranium and what is it used for?

2 How much longer will our supplies of coal, oil, natural gas and uranium last?

The Sun, wind and moving water can also be used as energy sources. These will never run out. They are **renewable**. Renewable energy sources are often called **alternative** energy sources.

Solar power uses sunlight. '**Solar panels**' absorb energy from the sun to heat water. The picture shows a solar power station. The solar panels heat water making steam which drives a turbine. Some houses have solar panels to make hot water for the house.

In the United Kingdom, 28% of our electricity is generated by nuclear power stations. In France, nuclear power stations generate 75% of the electricity

'**Solar cells**' are used to turn energy from the Sun directly into electricity. These can be used to provide electricity for small towns but they take up a lot of space. Solar cells are mainly used in small electrical items like calculators.

The world's first solar power station was built in 1969 in Odeillo, France

These solar cells provide electricity to nearby towns

3 a) What is a renewable energy source?

   b) Why do you think this is often described as an 'alternative' energy source?

   c) Is uranium an 'alternative' energy source? Explain your reasoning.

4 What is the difference between 'solar panels' and 'solar cells'?

5 a) What do you think are the advantages of using solar power?

   b) What are the disadvantages?

Wind turbines *are used to generate electricity from the wind. The wind turns the large blades, and the blades turn a generator*

Flowing water can be used to generate electrical energy in a **hydroelectric** power station. Waves and tides can also be used to generate electricity.

A **biomass** fuel is one that is obtained from plants and animals and their waste. This includes straw, cow dung, sewage and even rubbish. As these things rot away, methane gas is produced. This is the same gas as 'natural gas'

Wood is a biomass fuel. It has been used for thousands of years for heating and cooking. It is a renewable resource because trees can be re-grown.

Wind turbines would need to cover 370 km^2 to produce the same amount of energy as a nuclear power station. This is about the size of the Isle of Wight.

How would you show that energy can be produced from biomass?

How could you use this idea to keep plants warm in a cold-frame?

In Brazil, sugar cane is grown to be made into alcohol. The alcohol is mixed with petrol and used as a fuel for cars.

6 Why do you think there are very few hydroelectric power stations in the UK?

7 Where does the energy in biomass come from originally?

8 Write down three examples of using water to generate electricity.

9 Choose one of the alternative energy sources mentioned on this page. Say how it works and what you think the advantages and disadvantages of it are.

You should know...

● **What non-renewable and renewable energy sources are and examples of each.**

Which energy sources rely on the Sun?

Only three energy sources do not rely on the Sun. **Nuclear** power uses the nuclear energy stored in uranium, a metal found inside the Earth. **Tidal** power uses tides, caused by the gravity of the Moon. **Geothermal** power uses the heat from underground rocks.

Solar power uses sunlight directly, but other energy sources also rely on the Sun. Wind is caused by the Sun heating up the Earth. This is most easily seen at the coast. Air above the land is heated up quickly. It rises and is replaced by colder air from the sea. This makes a wind called a **convection current**. The wind can turn wind turbines, and also makes the waves used in wave power.

Solar panels have pipes inside. Energy from the Sun heats up water in the pipes. How could you find out what colour the pipes should be?
- What equipment would you need?
- How would you know which colour was best?

Clouds form from water evaporated by the heat of the Sun. Eventually the water falls back to Earth as rain. Hydroelectric power therefore depends on the Sun.

All fossil fuels and biomass fuels depend on the Sun. In plants, light energy is turned into chemical energy by photosynthesis. All living things depend on photosynthesis.

4 Explain why the chemical energy stored in a hamburger is originally from the Sun.

5 Unmuddle the names of these energy sources:
   i)   A GERM HOTEL
   ii) AN ULCER
   iii) TRICYCLE HORDE
   For each one, say:
   a) whether it depends on the Sun
   b) whether it is renewable or non-renewable.

6 Design a poster to show the many ways that the Sun helps us to produce electricity.

1 What sort of energy is stored inside uranium?

Energy from the Sun can be used to power an aeroplane.

2 Explain why wave power depends on the Sun.

3 Explain why hydro-electric power stations are not very useful in a drought.

You should know...
- **The energy sources used in geothermal, tidal and nuclear power are the only ones that do not depend on the Sun.**
- **The Sun is the original source of energy for most of our energy sources.**

Energy sources

What are the advantages and disadvantages of our energy sources?

All of our energy sources have advantages and disadvantages. The table lists some of them.

A geothermal power station

Energy source	Advantages	Disadvantages
Burning fossil fuels	Cheap	Non-renewable
		Produces gases which cause global warming and acid rain
Nuclear	Does not produce harmful gases	Expensive
		Non-renewable
		Produces dangerous radioactive substances that are difficult to get rid of
Solar	Clean	No electricity is produced if there is little Sun or at night
	Renewable	Solar panels do not collect very much heat energy
		Solar cells are expensive and take up a lot of space
Hydroelectric	Clean	Reservoirs take up huge amounts of space and destroy countryside
	Renewable	Only works in wet mountain regions
Wind	Clean	Electricity is not produced if there is no wind
	Renewable	Wind turbines are noisy and many of them are needed to make useful amounts of electricity. Some people think that they spoil the countryside
Geothermal	Clean	Only possible in certain parts of the world where hot rocks are near the surface of the Earth
	Cheap	
	Renewable	
Wave	Clean	Doesn't produce very much electricity
	Renewable	Will not work in calm waters
Tidal	Clean	Only works on rivers with big tides
	Renewable	
Biomass	Renewable	Burning produces gases that cause global warming

1 Which of the renewable energy sources would be best to use in your area? Explain why.

2 Which of the renewable energy sources would be useless in your area? Explain why.

3 Find out about 'global warming' and 'acid rain'. How does producing electricity by burning things help to cause these problems?

How is energy wasted in energy changes?

Energy cannot be made or destroyed. It can only be turned from one form into another. However, when this happens not all of the energy is turned into a form that we want.

When we run, some of our chemical energy is turned into moving energy (properly called **kinetic energy**). But we also get hot. Not all of the chemical energy from our food has been turned into kinetic energy. Some of it has been turned into heat energy. The heat energy is wasted energy.

 1 Draw an energy flow diagram showing the energy changes when someone runs.

NUTRITION		
Dry Pasta A 100 g serving of pasta weighs approx. 320 g when cooked		
TYPICAL COMPOSITION	A 100g (3½ oz) serving provides	
Energy	1463 kJ/345 kcal	
Protein	13.2 g	
Carbohydrate of which sugars	68.5g 2.0 g	
Fat of which saturates	2.0 g 0.4 g	
Fibre	2.9 g	
Sodium	trace	

The chemical energy in our bodies comes from the food that we eat. You will find the amount of chemical energy that a food contains printed on food packets. The unit for measuring energy is the **joule** (J). The energy on food packets is normally written in **kilojoules** (kJ). There are 1000 J in 1 kJ. Adults require about 12 000 kJ every day.

 2 Where does the chemical energy in our bodies come from?

3 What unit is energy measured in?

4 If a man eats 12 000 kJ in one day and all of this is used up by his muscles, how much heat energy does he produce?

Our muscles are not very efficient. For every 100 J of chemical energy a muscle receives, only 25 J are used for moving. 75 J of useless heat energy is also made. This means that only 25% of the chemical energy has been used to do something useful. Our muscles are only 25% efficient.

The unit for measuring energy is named after James Joule (1818–1889) who was from Salford, England. Although he was a brewer he did a lot of work on how energy was changed from one form to another and how it was never destroyed.

Useless heat energy is produced by machinery too. The moving parts of a car engine heat up, due to the force of friction. In a car only about 25% of the chemical energy stored in the fuel is turned into useful kinetic energy. Most of the rest is wasted as heat energy. The car is 25% efficient.

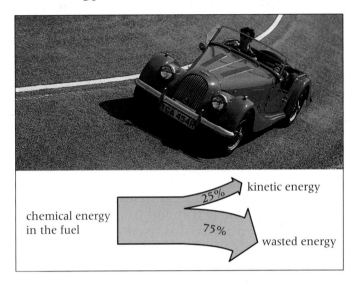

chemical energy in the fuel → 25% kinetic energy → 75% wasted energy

5 a) For each 100 J of chemical energy in the fuel of the car, how much becomes useful kinetic energy?
   b) What happens to the rest of the energy?

A fossil fuel power station has an efficiency of 30%. The rest is wasted as heat energy. For example, the generator produces useless heat energy as it turns.

6 a) What force can cause heat energy to be produced?
   b) Name one way to reduce this force.

7 a) The bulb in a torch needs electrical energy. What produces this?
   b) What energy is the electrical energy made from?
   c) What energies does the bulb produce?
   d) Which of these energies is the useful energy?
   e) Draw an energy flow diagram to show the energy changes in a torch.
   f) 70% of the energy made by the torch is wasted. How efficient is the torch?

8 What do we mean when we say how efficient something is?

Generators in power stations are filled with hydrogen. This gives less air resistance (or drag) than air, and so the generator produces less heat than if it were turning in air.

You should know...

● **When energy is changed from one form to another, useless heat energy is often produced.**

How can we use less of our non-renewable fuels?

Fossil fuels are running out. If we use less of them then they will last longer. Fossil fuels are used to generate electricity, for heating and for cooking.

 1 Write down the names of fossil fuels that are used for:
a) generating electricity
b) heating our homes
c) cooking.

If we stop some of the heat escaping from our homes we will use less fuel. We can do this by using materials that do not allow heat to go through them – **heat insulators**. Trapped air is a good heat insulator. Jumpers work because air is trapped in and keeps you warm. Trapped air is also used in double glazing and loft insulation for houses.

 2 Look at the photograph. How can we tell which homes have loft insulation?

 How would you find out which insulating material is the best?
- How could you set up your equipment?
- How could you find out how much energy is lost?
- How would you make your experiment a fair test?

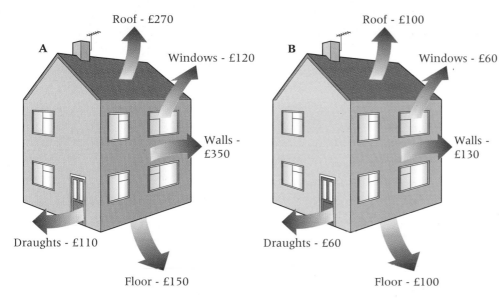

Roof - £270
Windows - £120
Walls - £350
Draughts - £110
Floor - £150

A

Roof - £100
Windows - £60
Walls - £130
Draughts - £60
Floor - £100

B

Houses lose different amounts of heat depending on how well insulated they are. This costs money in extra fuel bills.

Loft insulation comes in rolls of a material that has many pockets of trapped air

Heat loss through windows can be reduced by using double glazing. This also cuts down on noise from roads

Draught excluders are put around doors to stop draughts

The space in between the walls of a house can be filled with a blown mineral wool

You should know...

● **How heat loss can be reduced by using insulating materials containing trapped air.**

Look at the diagram of the two houses at the top of the page.

3 Which house has not been insulated?

4 a) For the uninsulated house, which part would you insulate first? Why?
   b) Which method of insulation would you choose?

5 Explain how double glazing works.

6 Look at the photograph showing the Integer house.
   a) How does the house absorb 'free' energy from the Sun?
   b) How does the house keep in the heat it has absorbed?

This house, built by INTEGER at Garston in Hertfordshire, has many features to save energy

Glossary

Pronunciation note: A capital 'O' is said as in 'so'

Abdomen	*ab-dO-men*	'Tail' section of an insect body.
Acid	*ass-id*	A substance that turns litmus red. Has a pH of less than 7.
Acid rain		Rain containing sulphuric acid and nitric acid.
Acne	*ack-nee*	Spots on the skin.
Adapted		When something is changed to help it do a particular thing. When the shape of a cell helps it do its job it is said to be 'adapted' to its job.
Adolescence	*add-ol-less-sense*	Time when both physical and emotional changes occur in humans.
Afterbirth		When the placenta is pushed out through the vagina.
Air resistance		A force that tries to slow things down that are moving through air. It is a type of friction.
Alkali	*alk-al-lie*	Substance that turns litmus blue. Has a pH of more than 7.
Aluminium		A metal used for carrying electricity because it is light and a good electrical conductor
Amnion	*am-nee-on*	Bag containing the amniotic fluid.
Amniotic fluid	*am-nee-ot-tick*	Liquid surrounding the growing embryo and protecting it.
Amphibian	*am-fib-ee-an*	Vertebrate with moist skin (e.g. frog)
Annelid	*ann-el-lid*	Invertebrate with a round, worm-like body in segments (e.g. earthworm).
Antacid	*ant-ass-id*	A medicine containing an alkali used to cancel out some of the acid in the stomach to treat heartburn.
Antenna		Singular of 'antennae'.
Antennae	*ann-ten-ee*	Feelers on the heads of insects. Singular = antenna.
Anther		Part of the stamen. It produces pollen grains.
Arachnid	*ar-ack-nid*	Arthropod with four pairs of legs (e.g. spider).
Arthropod	*arth-row-pod*	Invertebrate that has jointed legs (e.g. fly, spider).
Ascorbic acid		Chemical name for vitamin C.
Asexual reproduction		Producing new organisms from one parent only.
Asteroid	*ass-ter-oyd*	A small lump of rock orbiting around the Sun.
Atomic energy		Another word for nuclear energy
Axis	*acks-iss*	Imaginary vertical line that goes from one pole of the Earth to the other. The Earth turns around on this line.
Bacteria	*bac-teer-ry-ah*	Tiny living things that can cause disease.
Balanced forces		When two forces are the same strength, but working in opposite directions.
Biomass	*bi-O-mass*	Any fuel that comes from plants, animals, or their wastes (e.g. wood, methane from rotting plants, etc.)
Bird		Vertebrate with feathers (e.g. eagle)
Boiling point		When a liquid is at its boiling point it is as hot as it can get. It is evaporating as fast as it can.
Bonds		Forces holding particles together
Brain		Organ that controls what the body does.
Breathing	*bree-thing*	Taking in air and blowing out air.
Breathing system	*bree-thing*	Set of organs that allow breathing to happen.
Brine		A solution of common salt and water.
Capsule		A small space vehicle – a capsule usually only carries two or three people
Carpel	*car-pull*	Female reproductive organ found in flowers. Is made of a stigma, style and ovary.
Cell (in biology)	*sell*	The basic unit which living things are made of.
Cell (in physics)	*sell*	It contains a store of chemical energy that can produce electricity (the scientific name for a battery).
Cell division		One cell divides into two new cells.
Cell membrane	*sell mem-brain*	Controls what goes into and out of a living cell.
Cellulose	*sell-you-loze*	Substance from which cell walls are made.
Cell sap		Substance found inside a vacuole.
Cell wall		Tough wall around plant cells. Helps to support the cell.
Celsius	*sell-see-us*	Degrees Celsius – the units for temperature (°C).
Centipede	*sent-ip-eed*	Arthropod with long, thin body divided into sections. One pair of legs on each body section.
Cervix	*sir-vicks*	Ring of muscle at the bottom of the uterus in females.
Chemical energy		The kind of energy stored in chemicals. Food, fuels and batteries all contain chemical energy.
Chlorine	*klor-een*	A chemical added to water to kill bacteria.
Chlorophyll	*klor-O-fill*	Green substance found inside chloroplasts.
Chloroplast	*klor-O-plast*	Green disc containing chlorophyll. Found in plant cells and used to make food by photosynthesis.
Chromatogram	*krow-mat-O-gram*	The dried piece of paper produced by chromatography.
Chromatography	*krow-mat-og-graph-ee*	Separating dissolved solids from one another. The solids are usually coloured.
Chromosome	*crow-mow-sOme*	Thread-like strands contained in the nucleus, of cells. They contain the instructions for a living thing.
Ciliated	*silly-ay-ted*	Cells having cilia are 'ciliated'.
Ciliated epithelial cell	*silly-ay-ted eppy-theel-ee-al*	Cell found in the lungs.
Cilia	*silly-a*	Small hairs on the surface of some cells.
Circulatory system	*serk-you-late-or-ee*	Set of organs that carry oxygen and food around the body.
Circumcision	*sir-cum-siz-shun*	Removal of the foreskin.
Classification	*clas-if-ik-ay-shun*	Sorting things into groups.
Cnidarian	*nid-air-y-an*	Invertebrates with thin sack-like bodies (e.g. jellyfish).
Coal		A fossil fuel made from the remains of plants
Cold blooded		Animal with a body temperature that changes with the surroundings.
Common salt		A chemical we use to make things taste 'salty'.
Concentrate		We concentrate a solution by adding more of the solute to it.
Condenser		A piece of apparatus that cools down gases to turn them into liquids.
Condensing		A gas turning into a liquid.
Conduction	*con-duck-shun*	The way heat travels through solids.
Conductor		A material that lets energy travel through it easily.

Cone		Something used to carry the seeds of conifers.
Conifer	con-if-er	Plant with needle-shaped leaves. Reproduces using seeds found in cones.
Conservation of energy		See Law of Conservation of Energy
Constellation	con-stell-ay-shun	A pattern of stars.
Contact force		A force that needs to touch an object before it can affect it (e.g. friction).
Contraction	con-track-shun	When something is getting smaller.
Contractions	con-track-shuns	The uterus starts to push out the baby during labour.
Convection	con-veck-shun	A way that heat travels through liquids and gases.
Convection current	con-veck-shun	A flow of liquid or gas caused by part of it being heated or cooled more than the rest
Cord		Carries food, oxygen and waste between the placenta and the growing fetus.
Corrosive	cor-row-sive	Substances that attack metals, stonework and skin are called corrosive.
Coverslip		Thin piece of glass used to hold a specimen in place on a slide.
Cross-pollination		Transfer of pollen from an anther to a stigma of a different plant.
Crustacean	crust-ay-shun	Arthropod with chalky shell and 5–7 pairs of legs (e.g. lobster).
Cutting		A side stem is cut off a plant and allowed to sprout roots to make a new plant.
Cytoplasm	site-O-plaz-m	Jelly inside a cell where the cell's activities happen.
Daughter cells		The new cells formed in cell division.
Day		24 hours, the time it takes the Earth to spin once on its axis
Degrees Celsius	sell-see-us	Units for temperature (°C).
Density		The amount of mass that 1 cm^3 of a substance has. Measured in g/cm^3.
Desalination	dee-sall-in-ay-shun	Removing salt from sea water.
Diffusion		When particles mix with each other without anything moving them.
Digestive system	die-jest-iv	Set of organs used to break down food in our bodies.
Dilute		We dilute a solution by adding more of the solvent to it.
Dissolving	dizz-olv-ing	When a solid splits up and mixes with a liquid to make a solution.
Distillation		The process of separating a liquid from a solution by evaporating the liquid and then condensing it.
Double glazing		A way of insulating windows by trapping air between two layers of glass
Drag		Air resistance and water resistance are both sometimes called drag.
Earth		The planet we live on
Echinoderm	ek-eye-no-derm	Invertebrate that has a body in five parts (e.g. strafish).
Efficiency	ef-fish-en-see	A way of saying how much energy a something wastes
Efficient	ef-fish-ent	Something that does not waste much energy
Egg cell		The female sex cell (gamete).
Ejaculation	edge-ack-you-lay-shun	Semen is pumped out of a man's penis into the top of the vagina during sexual intercourse.
Elastic		Any substance that will return to its original shape and size after it has been stretched or squashed.

Electrical charges		Tiny pieces of material contained in the particles that things are made of. If the electrical charges are made to move, you get an electrical current.
Electrical conductor		A material that lets electricity flow through it easily
Electrical current		A flow of electrical charges. Another name for electricity.
Electrical energy		The kind of energy carried by electricity.
Electrical insulator		A material that does not let electricity flow through it easily
Electricity		A common word for 'electrical current'.
Elliptical	e-lip-tick-al	Oval shaped. The shape of a planet's orbit around the Sun.
Embryo (human)	em-bree-O	Tiny new human life which grows in the uterus.
Embryo (plant)	em-bree-O	Tiny plant, found inside a seed, with a very small shoot and a very small root.
Energy		Something that is needed to make things happen.
Energy flow diagram		A diagram to show energy changes.
Erection		When the penis becomes stiff.
Evaporating	Ev-ap-pour-ate-ing	A liquid turning into a gas.
Evaporation	ev-app-or-ay-shun	A liquid turning into a gas.
Excretion	ex-cree-shun	Getting rid of waste substances that have been made in the body by chemical reactions.
Excretory system	ex-cree-tor-ee	Set of organs that get rid of waste from our bodies.
Exoskeleton	ex-O-skel-e-ton	Thick outer covering found in arthropods.
Expansion	ecks-pan-shun	When something is getting bigger.
Extra terrestrial	extra terr-ess-tree-al	Something from another planet
Eyepiece lens		Part of the microscope you look down.
Fallopian tube		Carries egg cells from the ovaries to the uterus in women. Fertilisation happens here.
Fern		Plant that has many small waterproof leaves. Reproduces using spores.
Fertilisation	fert-ill-eyes-ay-shun	Joining of a male sex cell (gamete) with a female sex cell (gamete).
Fetus	fee-tus	After an embryo has grown all its organs it is called a fetus. This is usually after about 10 weeks.
Filament		Part of the stamen in flowers. It supports the anther.
Filter		Something with small holes in it used in filtering.
Filtering		Separating things that have not dissolved from a liquid. The liquid is passed through a filter to do this.
Fish		Vertebrate with wet scales (e.g. salmon)
Flatworm		Invertebrate with flat, worm-like body (e.g. tapeworm).
Flower		Organ containing smaller reproductive organs – carpel (female), stamen (male).
Flowering plant		Plant with large, flat leaves. Reproduces using seeds found in fruits. Fruits and seeds form inside flowers.
Focusing wheel		Part of a microscope that allows you to see clearly.
Force		A push or a pull.
Force meter		Piece of equipment, containing a spring, used to measure forces.
Foreskin		A covering of skin protecting the head of the penis.
Fossil		A dead organism that has been trapped in mud and whose body has not completely rotted away.

Fossil fuels		Coal, oil and gas – all fuels that were formed from the remains of dead plants and animals
Fractionating tower	*frac-shon-ay-ting*	Large tower used to separate the different liquids in crude oil.
Freezing		A liquid turning into a solid.
Freezing point		The temperature at which a liquid turns into a solid.
Friction		A force that tries to slow things down when two things rub against each other.
Fruit		Something used to carry the seeds of flowering plants. Can be fleshy or dry.
Fuel		Anything that stores an energy that can be converted into heat energy – includes fossil fuels and nuclear fuel
Full Moon		The phase of the Moon when it looks like a bright, full circle.
Galaxy		Millions of stars grouped together.
Gamete	*gam-meet*	Scientific word for sex cell.
Gas		See natural gas
Gas		Something made of particles that are very spread out and have no bonds between them.
Generate		Make electricity by turning a magnet inside coils of wire
Generator		Large coil of wire with a magnet inside. When the magnet is turned, electricity is produced in the coil of wire.
Geothermal power	*gee-O-therm-al*	Making electricity using heat from hot rocks underground.
Germination	*germ-in-ay-shun*	When a seed first starts to grow.
Glands		The glands in the male reproductive system add a special liquid to the sperm cells to make semen. There are other sorts of glands in the body.
Global warming		Another term for 'greenhouse effect'.
Gram		A unit for measuring mass (g).
Gravitational potential energy	*grav-it-ay-shon-al*	The kind of energy stored by anything that can fall to the ground.
Gravity		The force of attraction between any two objects. The Earth is very big and so has a large gravity pulling everything down towards it.
Greenhouse effect		When the Earth warms up more than it should. It is caused by certain gases (like carbon dioxide) keeping heat in the Earth's atmosphere.
Hazard warning symbol		Sign on a container showing what the dangers of the substance inside are.
Heart		Organ that pumps blood.
Heat conductor		A material that lets heat energy flow through it easily
Heat energy		The hotter something is, the more heat energy it has.
Heat exchanger		Piece of equipment used in desalination to take heat away from steam and turn it into water.
Heat insulator		A material that does not let heat energy flow through it easily
Hemispheres	*hem-ee-sfears*	The two halves of a sphere – the shape you would get if you cut a ball in half
Herb		Plant with a strong flavour used in cooking.
Hydroelectric power	*hi-drO-el-eck-trick*	Making electricity by letting falling water (usually from a reservoir) turn turbines and generators
Image		What you see down a microscope.
Implantation	*im-plant-ay-shun*	When an embryo sinks into the soft lining of the uterus.

Indicator	*ind-ic-ay-ter*	A dye that will change colour in acids and alkalis.
Inner planets		Mercury, Venus, Earth and Mars. The inner planets are all rocky planets.
Insect		Arthropod with three pairs of legs (e.g. fly).
Insoluble		A solid that will not dissolve.
Insulator	*ins-you-lay-ter*	A material that does not let energy flow through it.
Intestine	*in-test-in*	Small intestine is an organ used to digest and absorb food. Large intestine removes water from unwanted food.
Invertebrate	*in-vert-eb-rate*	Animal with no backbone.
Irrigation	*irr-ig-ay-shun*	Watering crops by using channels or pipes.
IVF		Stands for In Vitro Fertilisation. Using modern science to help people have babies.
Joule	*jool*	The unit for measuring energy (J).
Key		Branching and statement keys. Both are used to work out what something is.
Kidneys		Organs used to clean the blood and make urine.
Kilogram		A unit for measuring mass (kg). There are 1000 g in 1 kg.
Kilojoule	*kill-O-jool*	There are 1000 joules (J) in 1 kilojoule (kJ)
Kinetic energy	*kin-et-ick*	The kind of energy in moving things.
Kingdom		Largest groups that living things are sorted into. The two biggest are the plant kingdom and the animal kingdom.
Labour		Time when the baby is about to be born.
Larva		Young insect which is not yet an adult.
Larvae	*larv-ee*	Plural of 'larva'.
Law of conservation of energy		The idea that energy can never be created or destroyed, only changed from one form into another
Leaf		Plant organ used to make food using photosynthesis.
Leap year		A year with 366 days in it. We have a leap year every 4 years
Life processes		Seven things that all living things must do: movement, reproduction, sensitivity, growth, respiration, excretion and nutrition.
Light energy		The kind of energy given out by light bulbs, candles, etc.
Light year		The distance that light travels in one year.
Liquid	*lick-wid*	Something made of particles fairly close together, but with bonds that are less strong than in solids. The particles can move past each other in a liquid.
Litmus		A simple kind of indicator. It is red in acids and blue in alkalis.
Liver		Organ used to make and destroy substances in our bodies.
Lubricant	*loo-brick-ant*	A substance (normally a liquid) used to reduce friction.
Lubrication	*loo-brick-ay-shun*	Adding a lubricant to something.
Lunar month		28 days – the time it takes the Moon to orbit around the Earth once
Lungs		Organs used to take oxygen out of the air and put waste carbon dioxide into the air.
Machine		Something that changes energy from one form to another
Magnetism		A force that attracts objects made out of iron.
Magnification	*mag-nif-ick-ay-shun*	How much bigger a drawing or an image is compared to real life.

Mains electricity		Electricity supplied to homes and factories through the National Grid
Mammal		Vertebrate with hair and produces milk (e.g. human).
Mammary glands		Glands contained in the breasts of women which produce milk after childbirth.
Mass		The amount of matter that something is made of. Measured in grams (g) and kilograms (kg). Your mass does not change if you go into space or to another planet.
Melting		A solid turning into a liquid.
Melting point		The temperature at which a solid turns into a liquid.
Menopause	*men-O-paws*	When the ovaries in women stop releasing egg cells.
Menstrual cycle	*men-strew-al*	Series of events lasting about 28 days, happening in the female reproductive system. The cycle causes ovulation and the lining of the uterus to be replaced.
Menstruation	*men-strew-ay-shun*	When the lining of the uterus and a little blood pass out of the vagina as part of the menstrual cycle.
Metamorphosis	*met-a-mor-fos-iss*	The series of changes in an insect from larva to adult.
Microscope	*my-crow-scope*	Used to magnify small things.
Milky way		The galaxy that our Solar System is in.
Millipede		Arthropod with long, thin body divided into sections. Two pairs of legs on each body section.
Mineral		A chemical that is useful or beautiful to look at.
Mineral salt		Chemicals found in the soil that plants need to grow healthily.
Mixture		A lot of different things jumbled up together.
Mollusc	*moll-usk*	Invertebrate that crawls on a fleshy pad (e.g. snail).
Moon		A moon is a large lump of rock orbiting around a planet. The Earth is orbited by 'the Moon'.
Moss		Plant with no roots and no xylem and many thin leaves. Reproduces using spores
Mould		A type of fungus that rots things away.
Moulting	*molt-ing*	When a young insect gets rid of its exoskelton so that it can grow.
Muscle cell	*muss-ell*	Cell that can change its length and so help us to move.
National Grid		System of overhead and underground cables that carry electricity around the country
Natural gas		Fossil fuel formed from the remains of dead sea creatures
Natural satellite		Something orbiting a planet that is not man-made (e.g. the Moon).
Navel	*nave-ell*	Scar left by the cord. Often called the 'belly-button'.
Nectary		Produces sugary nectar to attract insects. Part of a flower.
Nerve cell		Cell that carries messages around the body.
Nervous system	*nerve-us*	Set of organs that help to carry messages around the body.
Neutral		Substance that is not an acid or an alkali. Has a pH of 7.
New Moon		The phase of the Moon when you can hardly see it. The whole of the lit side is pointing away from the Earth.
Newton		The unit of force (N).

Newton meter		Another name for a force meter.
Nitrate	*night-rate*	The most important mineral salt needed by plants.
Non-contact force		A force that can affect something from a distance (e.g. gravity).
Non-renewable energy source		Any energy source that will run out and we cannot renew our supplies of it (e.g. oil).
Northern hemisphere		The half of the Earth with the North Pole in it. The UK is in the northern hemisphere.
Nuclear energy		Energy stored inside the particles that things are made out of.
Nuclear power		Making electricity by using the nuclear energy stored inside uranium.
Nucleus	*new-clee-us*	Controls what a cell does.
Nutrient	*new-tree-ent*	A substance that a living thing needs so it can grow healthily.
Nutrition	*new-trish-un*	Getting food. Animals need to eat but plants can make their own.
Objective lens		Part of the microscope that is closest to what you are looking at.
Observation		What you can see happening in an experiment.
Oil		Fossil fuel formed from the remains of dead sea creatures
Opaque	*O-pake*	Something that you cannot see through.
Orbit		The path a planet takes around the Sun, or the path a moon or satellite takes around a planet
Organ		A group of different tissues working together to do an important job.
Organ system		Collection of organs working together to do a very important job.
Organism	*org-an-is-m*	Any living thing. An organism must do all seven of the 'life processes'.
Outer planets		Jupiter, Saturn, Uranus, Neptune and Pluto. All the outer planets except Pluto are made of gas.
Ova	*O-va*	Another name for egg cells. The singular is ovum.
Ovary (humans)	*O-very*	Female reproductive organ. Produces egg cells.
Ovary (plants)	*O-very*	Part of the carpel. It contains ovules each of which contains an egg cell.
Ovulation	*ov-you-lay-shun*	Release of an egg cell from an ovary in women.
Ovule	*ov-you'll*	Contains egg cells in plants. Is found in the ovary.
Oxygen	*ocks-ee-jen*	A gas in the air used in respiration.
Pallisade cell	*pall-iss-aid*	Cell found in leaves which contains many chloroplasts.
Particles	*part-ick-als*	The tiny pieces that everything is made out of.
Petals		Brightly coloured and/or heavily scented part of a flower. They attract insects.
pH scale		A numbered scale from 1–14 showing the strengths of acids and alkalis. Numbers below 7 are acids. Numbers above 7 are alkalis. pH 7 is neutral.
Phases of the Moon		The different shapes that the Moon seems to have at different times.
Photosynthesis	*foto-sinth-e-sis*	Process that plants use to make their own food. It needs light to work. Carbon dioxide and water are used up. Food (a sugar called glucose) and oxygen are produced.
Placenta	*plas-en-ta*	Attached to the uterus wall, this takes oxygen and food out of the mother's blood and puts waste materials into the mother's blood.
Planet		Something that orbits a star
Plant crossing		Producing new varieties of plants by pollination between different varieties.

Pollen		The male sex cell (gamete) in plants.
Pollen tube		Tube that grows from a pollen grain down through the stigma and style and into the ovary.
Pollination	poll-in-**ay**-shun	Transfer of pollen from an anther to a stigma.
Pollinator		An animal that carries pollen between plants.
Potential energy	pO-**ten**-shall	The scientific word for 'stored' energy
Prediction		What you think will happen in an experiment.
Pregnant		When a woman has an embryo growing inside her uterus.
Premature baby		A small baby born early.
Pressure	**presh**-ur	The amount of force on a certain area. The force is caused by particles hitting that area.
Property		Something used to describe how a material behaves and what it is like. Hardness is a property of some solids.
Protein	**pro**-teen	Important substance that is used for growth.
Puberty	**pew**-bert-ty	Time when physical changes happen in the body between the ages of about 11 and 15.
Pupa	**pew**-pa	Protective case in which a young insect (larva) turns into an adult.
Pupae	**pew**-pee	Plural of 'pupa'.
Pure water		Water that does not have anything dissolved in it.
Radiation	ray-dee-**ay**-shun	The way heat travels through space or transparent materials.
Radioactivity		Dangerous particles and energy given off by uranium and other radioactive materials
Rechargeable	ree-**charge**-ab-el	Cells that can have more energy stored in them after they have been used are said to be rechargeable.
Recycling	re-**sye**-cling	Making use of things that have been thrown away.
Renewable energy source		An energy source that will never run out (e.g. solar power).
Reproduction	ree-pro-**duck**-shun	Producing new organisms that are like the parents.
Reproductive organs		Organs used in sexual reproduction. Some of them produce gametes.
Reproductive system		All the reproductive organs.
Reptile		Vertebrate with dry scales (e.g. snake).
Reservoir	**rez**-zer-vwarr	Man-made lake.
Respiration	ress-per-**ay**-shun	Process that uses up oxygen and food to release energy from food. Carbon dioxide is produced as a waste gas.
Robot		A machine that has a computer to control it. It does not have to receive instructions or controls from a human.
Room temperature		About 20 °C.
Root		Plant organ used to take water out of the soil.
Root hair cell		Cell found in roots. The root hair has a large surface area to help the cell absorb water quickly.
Roundworm		Invertebrates with round worm-like bodies but no segments (e.g. hookworm)
Runner		Shoots used for asexual reproduction in some plants (e.g. strawberry).
Salts		Chemicals from rocks that have dissolved in water.
Satellite		Anything that orbits a planet.
Saturated		When a solution contains as much dissolved solid as it possibly can it is 'saturated'.

Srotum	**scrow**-tum	Bag of skin containing the testes in males.
Seed coat		Hard outer covering of a seed
Seed dispersal		Spreading seeds away from the parent plant.
Seedling		When a new plant has formed its first leaves it is called a seedling.
Seeds		Grow into new plants. Made by conifers and flowering plants.
Self-pollination		Transfer of pollen from an anther to stigma of the same plant.
Semen	**see**-men	A mixture of sperm cells and fluids released by men during sexual intercourse.
Sensitivity	sen-sit-**iv**-it-ee	Ability to sense things in the surroundings.
Sepal	**sep**-al	Small green leaf used to protect the flower in bud.
Sex hormones	**hor**-moans	Chemicals released in our bodies that control puberty.
Sexual reproduction	re-pro-**duck**-shun	Producing new organisms by combining a male and a female gamete.
Skin		Organ used for protection and feeling.
Slide		Glass sheet that a specimen is put on.
Sodium chloride	sow-dee-um **klor**-ide	Chemical name for common salt.
Solar cells		Flat plates that convert light energy into electrical energy.
Solar panels		Flat plates that use the Sun's energy to heat water.
Solar power		Making electricity by using light or heat energy from the Sun.
Solar system		A star with planets and other objects orbiting it.
Solid		Something made of particles very close together, held by strong bonds.
Solubility	sol-you-**bill**-ity	The amount of a solid that will dissolve in 100 g of a liquid.
Soluble	sol-you-bull	A solid that can dissolve in a liquid. Salt is soluble in water.
Solute		The solid that has dissolved in a liquid to make a solution.
Solution	sol-**oo**-shun	When a solid has dissolved in a liquid.
Solvent		The liquid that has dissolved a solid to make a solution.
Sound energy		The kind of energy made by anything that is making a noise.
Space probe		An unmanned space craft that has cameras and other equipment to find out about other planets.
Space station		A man-made satellite orbiting around the Earth, big enough for several astronauts to live in for months or years
Species	**spee**-sees	Each different type of living thing (e.g. lions and tigers are similar, but different species).
Specimen	**spess**-im-men	What you look at down a microscope.
Speed		How fast something is moving. Often measured in metres per second (m/s).
Sperm cell		The male sex cell (gamete) in humans.
Sperm duct		Tube that carries sperm from the testes to the urethra.
Sphere	**sfear**	A shape like a ball
Spice		Part of a plant with a strong flavour used to flavour food.
Spiracles	**spir**-ack-als	Small breathing holes on an insect's abdomen.
Sponge		Invertebrate with a body made of loosely joined cells.

Spore		Very small part of a plant that can grow into a new plant. Made by mosses and ferns.
Stage		Part of the microscope. You put things on it.
Stain		Dye used to colour parts of a cell to make them easier to see.
Stamen	*stay-men*	Male reproductive organ found in flowers. It is made of an anther and a filament.
Star		A large ball of gas that gives off lots of heat and light. The Sun is a star.
Starch		Substance that plants use as a store of food.
States of matter		There are three different forms in which a substance can be in; solid, liquid and gas. These are the three states of matter.
Static electricity		A force which attracts things with extra electrical charges on them.
Steam		Water as a gas. Also called water vapour.
Stem		Plant organ used to take water to the leaves and to support the leaves.
Stigma		Part of the carpel. It is where pollen lands.
Still		The apparatus used for distillation.
Stoma	*stO-ma*	Singular of stomata.
Stomach	*stum-ack*	Organ used to help break up food.
Stomata	*stom-**mart**-a*	Small holes on the undersides of leaves which let gases into and out of the leaf.
Strain energy		The kind of energy stored in stretched or squashed things which can bounce back to their original shapes.
Style		Part of the carpel connecting the stigma to the ovary.
Sublimation		Going from solid to gas without becoming a liquid.
Sun		The star that the Earth orbits around.
Telescope		An instrument that helps us to see distant things like the stars or planets
Temperature		How hot or cold something is. Measured in degrees Celsius (°C).
Testes		Plural of 'testis'.
Testis		Male reproductive organ in human males. Produces sperm cells.
Theory	*thear-ree*	An idea about why things work the way they do. Scientists use their imaginations to come up with a theory.
Thorax		Middle section of an insect body.
Tidal power		Making electricity using the moving (kinetic) energy from tides.
Tissue	*tiss-you*	A group of the same cells all doing the same job.
Toxic	*tocks-ick*	Another word for poisonous.
Transformer		Piece of equipment used to change voltages.
Transparent		Another word for see-through.
Tuber	*tube-er*	Underground storage organ used for asexual reproduction in some plants (e.g. potato).
Umbilical cord	*Um-**bill**-ick-al*	See 'cord'

Unbalanced forces		When two forces working in opposite directions are not the same strength.
Universal indicator		A mixture of indicators giving a different colour depending on how weak or strong an acid or an alkali is.
Universe		All the galaxies and the space between them make up the universe.
Unmanned		Something that has no humans on it.
Upthrust		A force that pushes things up.
Uranium	*yer-**rain**-ee-um*	A fuel used in nuclear power stations.
Urethra	*you-**ree**-thra*	A tube carrying semen or urine running down the centre of the penis in males. A tube carrying urine in females.
Uterus	*you-ter-ous*	Area in females in which a baby develops.
Vacuole	*vack-you-oll*	Storage space in plant cells.
Vacuum	*vack-youm*	A completely empty space.
Vagina	*vaj-I-na*	Tube in females. The penis is placed here during sexual intercourse.
Variable	*vair-ri-able*	A factor in an experiment that can change.
Variety		A plant or animal that is different in some way from its parents.
Vertebrate	*vert-eb-rate*	An animal with a backbone.
Voltage		The amount of pushing that a cell does is called the voltage.
Volts		The unit of voltage (V).
Volume		The amount of space that something takes up. Measured in cm^3.
Warm blooded		Animal that keep its body temperature the same.
Wasted energy		Energy that is not useful.
Water resistance		A force that tries to slow things down that are moving through water. It is a type of friction.
Water transport system		Set of organs carrying water from the roots of a plant to its leaves.
Water vapour	*vay-per*	Water as a gas. Also called steam.
Wave power		Making electricity using the waves in the sea as a source of energy.
Weight		The amount of force with which gravity pulls something towards the Earth. It is measured in Newtons (N).
Wilting		When the leaves on a plant droop due to lack of water.
Wind chill		When it feels colder than the actual temperature because of the wind.
Wind turbine		A kind of windmill that generates electricity using energy from the wind
Xylem tubes	*z-eye-lem*	Special tubes that carry water in plants.
Year		The length of time it takes a planet to go around the Sun. One year on Earth is 365.25 days.
Zygote	*z-eye-goat*	Fertilised egg cell. Formed by a male and a female gamete joining together.

Index